SCIENCE NEWS

31

SCIENCE
NEWS

EDITED BY A. W. HASLETT

31

PENGUIN BOOKS

MELBOURNE : LONDON : BALTIMORE

First published February 1954

*

Subscriptions to

SCIENCE NEWS

*(which appears quarterly in
February, May, August, and November)
and*

NEW BIOLOGY

*(which appears half-yearly in
April and October)
are accepted at 9s each
for four issues
including postage*

*

*Made and printed in Great Britain
for Penguin Books Ltd
Harmondsworth, Middlesex
by The Campfield Press, St Albans*

CONTENTS

26 illustrations are between pages 64 and 65

SOLVABLE AND UNSOLVABLE
PROBLEMS

A. M. TURING, F.R.S.

IF one is given a puzzle to solve one will usually, if it proves to be difficult, ask the owner whether it can be done. Such a question should have a quite definite answer, yes or no, at any rate provided the rules describing what you are allowed to do are perfectly clear. Of course the owner of the puzzle may not know the answer. One might equally ask, 'How can one tell whether a puzzle is solvable?', but this cannot be answered so straightforwardly. The fact of the matter is that there is *no* systematic method of testing puzzles to see whether they are solvable or not. If by this one meant merely that nobody had ever yet found a test which could be applied to any puzzle, there would be nothing at all remarkable in the statement. It would have been a great achievement to have invented such a test, so we can hardly be surprised that it has never been done. But it is not merely that the test has never been found. It has been proved that no such test ever can be found.

Let us get away from generalities a little and consider a particular puzzle. One which has been on sale during the last few years and has probably been seen by most of the readers of this article illustrates a number of the points involved quite well. The puzzle consists of a large square within which are some smaller movable squares numbered 1 to 15, and one empty space, into which any of the neighbouring squares can be slid leaving a new empty space behind it. One may be asked to transform a given arrangement of the squares into another by a succession of such movements of a square into an empty space. For this puzzle there is a fairly simple and quite practicable rule by which one can tell whether the transformation required is possible or not. One first imagines the transformation carried out according to a different set of rules. As well as sliding the squares into the empty space one is allowed to make moves each consisting of two interchanges, each of one pair of squares. One would, for instance, be allowed as one move to interchange the squares numbered 4 and 7, and also the squares numbered 3 and 5. One is permitted to use the same number in both pairs. Thus one may replace 1 by 2, 2 by 3, and 3 by 1 as a move because this is the same as interchanging first (1, 2) and then (1, 3). The original puzzle is solvable by sliding if it is solvable according to the new rules. It is not solvable by sliding if the required position can be reached by the new rules, together with a 'cheat' consisting of *one single* interchange of a pair of squares.* Suppose, for instance, that one is asked to get back to the standard position –

<table>
<tr><td>1</td><td>2</td><td>3</td><td>4</td></tr>
<tr><td>5</td><td>6</td><td>7</td><td>8</td></tr>
<tr><td>9</td><td>10</td><td>11</td><td>12</td></tr>
<tr><td>13</td><td>14</td><td>15</td><td>▨</td></tr>
</table>

from the position

<table>
<tr><td>10</td><td>1</td><td>4</td><td>5</td></tr>
<tr><td>9</td><td>2</td><td>6</td><td>8</td></tr>
<tr><td>11</td><td>3</td><td>▨</td><td>15</td></tr>
<tr><td>13</td><td>14</td><td>7</td><td>12</td></tr>
</table>

One may, according to the modified rules, first get the empty square into the correct position by moving the squares 15 and 12, and then get the squares 1, 2, 3, . . . successively into their correct positions by the interchanges (1, 10), (2, 10), (3, 4), (4, 5), (5, 9), (6, 10), (7, 10), (9, 11), (10, 11), (11, 15). The squares 8, 12, 13, 14, 15 are found to be already in their correct positions when their turns are reached. Since the number of interchanges required is

---

*It would take us too far from our main purpose to give the proof of this rule: the reader should have little difficulty in proving it by making use of the fact that an odd number of interchanges can never bring a set of objects back to the position it started from.

even, this transformation is possible by sliding.† If one were required after this to interchange say square 14 and 15 it could not be done.

This explanation of the theory of the puzzle can be regarded as entirely satisfactory. It gives one a simple rule for determining for any two positions whether one can get from one to the other or not. That the rule is so satisfactory depends very largely on the fact that it does not take very long to apply. No mathematical method can be useful for any problem if it involves much calculation. It is nevertheless sometimes interesting to consider whether something is possible at all or not, without worrying whether, in case it *is* possible, the amount of labour or calculation is economically prohibitive. These investigations that are not concerned with the amount of work involved are in some ways easier to carry out, and they certainly have a greater aesthetic appeal. The results are not altogether without value, for if one has proved that there is no method of doing something it follows *a fortiori* that there is no practicable method. On the other hand, if one method has been proved to exist by which the decision can be made, it gives some encouragement to anyone who wishes to find a workable method.

From this point of view, in which one is only interested in the question, 'Is there a systematic way of deciding whether puzzles of this kind are solvable?', the rules which have been described for the sliding-squares puzzle are much more special and detailed than is really necessary. It would be quite enough to say: 'Certainly one can find out whether one position can be reached from another by a systematic procedure. There are only a finite number of positions in which the numbered squares can be arranged (viz. 20922789888000) and only a finite number (2, 3, or 4) of moves in each position. By making a list of all the

†It can in fact be done by sliding successively the squares numbered 7, 14, 13, 11, 9, 10, 1, 2, 3, 7, 15, 8, 5, 4, 6, 3, 10, 1, 2, 6, 3, 10, 6, 2, 1, 6, 7, 15, 8, 5, 10, 8, 5, 10, 8, 7, 6, 9, 15, 5, 10, 8, 7, 6, 5, 15, 9, 5, 6, 7, 8, 12, 14, 13, 15, 10, 13, 15, 11, 9, 10, 11, 15, 13, 12, 14, 13, 15, 9, 10, 11, 12, 14, 13, 15, 14, 13, 15, 14, 13, 12, 11, 10, 9, 13, 14, 15, 12, 11, 10, 9, 13, 14, 15.

positions and working through all the moves, one can divide the positions into classes, such that sliding the squares allows one to get to any position which is in the same class as the one started from. By looking up which classes the two positions belong to one can tell whether one can get from one to the other or not.' This is all, of course, perfectly true, but one would hardly find such remarks helpful if they were made in reply to a request for an explanation of how the puzzle should be done. In fact they are so obvious that under such circumstances one might find them somehow rather insulting. But the fact of the matter is, that if one is interested in the question as put, 'Can one tell by a systematic method in which cases the puzzle is solvable?', this answer is entirely appropriate, because one wants to know if there is a systematic method, rather than to know of a good one.

The same kind of argument will apply for any puzzle where one is allowed to move certain 'pieces' around in a specified manner, provided that the total number of essentially different positions which the pieces can take up is finite. A slight variation on the argument is necessary in general to allow for the fact that in many puzzles some moves are allowed which one is not permitted to reverse. But one can still make a list of the positions, and list against these first the positions which can be reached from them in one move. One then adds the positions which are reached by two moves and so on until an increase in the number of moves does not give rise to any further entries. For instance, we can say at once that there is a method of deciding whether a patience can be got out with a given order of the cards in the pack: it is to be understood that there is only a finite number of places in which a card is ever to be placed on the table. It may be argued that one is permitted to put the cards down in a manner which is not perfectly regular, but one can still say that there is only a finite number of 'essentially different' positions. A more interesting example is provided by those puzzles made (apparently at least) of two or more pieces of very thick twisted wire which one is required to separate. It is understood that one is not allowed to bend the wires at all, and when one makes the right movement there is always plenty of room to get the pieces apart without them ever touching, if one wishes to do so. One may describe the positions of the pieces by saying where some three definite points of each piece are. Because of the spare space it is not necessary to give these positions quite exactly. It would be enough to give them to, say, a tenth of a millimetre. One does not need to take any notice of movements of the puzzle as a whole: in fact one could suppose one of the pieces quite fixed. The second piece can be supposed to be not very far away, for, if it is, the puzzle is already solved. These considerations enable us to reduce the number of 'essentially different' positions to a finite number, probably a few hundred millions, and the usual argument will then apply. There are some further complications, which we will not consider in detail, if we do not know how much clearance to allow for. It is necessary to repeat the process again and again allowing successively smaller and smaller clearances. Eventually one will find that either it can be solved, allowing a small clearance margin, or else it cannot be solved even allowing a small margin of 'cheating' (i.e. of 'forcing', or having the pieces slightly overlapping in space). It will, of course, be understood that this process of trying out the possible positions is not to be done with the physical puzzle itself, but on paper, with mathematical descriptions of the positions, and mathematical criteria for deciding whether in a given position the pieces overlap, etc.

These puzzles where one is asked to separate rigid bodies are in a way like the 'puzzle' of trying to undo a tangle, or more generally of trying to turn one knot into another without cutting the string. The difference is that one is allowed to bend the string, but not the wire forming the rigid bodies. In either case, if one wants to treat the problem seriously and systematically one has to replace the physical puzzle by a mathematical equivalent. The knot puzzle lends itself quite conveniently to this. A knot is just a closed curve in three dimensions nowhere crossing itself; but, for the purpose we are interested in, any knot can be given accurately enough as a series of segments in the directions of the three coordinate axes. Thus, for instance, the trefoil knot (Figure 1*a*) may be regarded as consisting of a number of segments joining the points given, in the usual (x, y, z) system of coordinates, as $(1, 1, 1)$, $(4, 1, 1,)$, $(4, 2, 1)$, $(4, 2, -1)$, $(2, 2, -1)$, $(2, 2, 2)$, $(2, 0, 2)$, $(3, 0, 2)$, $(3, 0, 0)$, $(3, 3, 0)$, $(1, 3, 0)$, $(1, 3, 1)$ and returning again with a twelfth segment to the starting point $(1, 1, 1)$. This representation of the knot is shown in perspective in Figure 1b. There is no special virtue in the representation which has been chosen. If it is desired to follow the original curve more closely a greater number of segments must be used. Now let a and d represent unit steps in the positive and negative X-directions respectively, b and e in the Y-directions, and c and f in the Z-directions: then this knot may be described as *aaabffddccceeaffbbbddcee*. One can then, if one wishes, deal entirely with such sequences of letters. In order that such a sequence should represent a knot it is necessary and sufficient that the numbers of a's and d's should be equal, and likewise the number of b's equal to the number of e's and the number of c's equal to the number of f's, and it must not be possible to obtain another sequence of letters with these properties by omitting a number of consecutive letters at the beginning or the end or both. One can turn a knot into an equivalent one by operations of the following kinds—

(i) One may move a letter from one end of the row to the other.

(ii) One may interchange two consecutive letters provided this still gives a knot.

(iii) One may introduce a letter a in one place in the row, and d somewhere else, or b and e, or c and f, or take such pairs out, provided it still gives a knot.

(iv) One may replace a everywhere by aa and d by dd or replace each b and e by bb and ee or each c and f by cc and ff. One may also reverse any such operation.

—and these are all the moves that are necessary.

It is also possible to give a similar symbolic equivalent for the problem of separating rigid bodies, but it is less straightforward than in the case of knots.

These knots provide an example of a puzzle where one cannot tell in advance how many arrangements of pieces may be involved (in this case the pieces are the letters a, b, c, d. e, f), so that

(a)

(b)

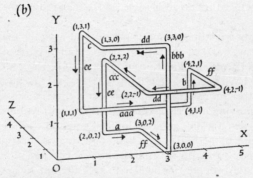

Fig. 1. (a) The trefoil knot (b) a possible representation of this knot as a number of segments joining points.

the usual method of determining whether the puzzle is solvable cannot be applied. Because of rules (iii) and (iv) the lengths of the sequences describing the knots may become indefinitely great. No systematic method is yet known by which one can tell whether two knots are the same.

Another type of puzzle which we shall find very important is the 'substitution puzzle'. In such a puzzle one is supposed to be supplied with a finite number of different kinds of counters, perhaps just black (*B*) and white (*W*). Each kind is in unlimited supply. Initially a number of counters are arranged in a row and one is asked to transform it into another pattern by substitutions. A finite list of the substitutions allowed is given. Thus, for instance, one might be allowed the substitutions

(i) $WBW \rightarrow B$

(ii) $BW \rightarrow WBBW$

and be asked to transform WBW into $WBBBW$, which could be done as follows

$$WBW \rightarrow WWBBW \rightarrow WWBWBBW \rightarrow WBBBW$$
$$\underline{\quad} \text{(ii)} \quad \overline{\underline{\quad}} \text{(ii)} \quad \overline{\underline{\quad}} \text{(i)}$$

Here the substitutions used are indicated by the numbers below the arrows, and their effects by underlinings. On the other hand if one were asked to transform WBB into BW it could not be done, for there are no admissible steps which reduce the number of B's.

It will be seen that with this puzzle, and with the majority of substitution puzzles, one cannot set any bound to the number of positions that the original position might give rise to.

It will have been realized by now that a puzzle can be something rather more important than just a toy. For instance the task of proving a given mathematical theorem within an axiomatic system is a very good example of a puzzle.

It would be helpful if one had some kind of 'normal form' or 'standard form' for describing puzzles. There is, in fact, quite a reasonably simple one which I shall attempt to describe. It will be necessary for reasons of space to take a good deal for granted, but this need not obscure the main ideas. First of all we may suppose that the puzzle is somehow reduced to a mathematical form in the sort of way that was used in the case of the knots. The position of the puzzle may be described, as was done in that case, by sequences of symbols in a row. There is usually very little difficulty in reducing other arrangements of symbols (e.g. the squares in the sliding squares puzzle) to this form. The question which remains to be answered is, 'What sort of rules should one be allowed to have for rearranging the symbols or counters?' In order to answer this one needs to think about what kinds of processes ever do occur in such rules, and, in order to reduce their number, to break them up into simpler processes. Typical of such processes are counting, copying, comparing, substituting. When one is doing such processes, it is necessary, especially if there are many symbols involved, and if one wishes to avoid carrying too much information in one's head, either to make a number of jottings elsewhere or to use a number of marker objects as well as the pieces of the puzzle itself. For instance, if one were making a copy of a row of counters concerned in the puzzle it would be as well to have a marker which divided the pieces which have been copied from those which have not and another showing the end of the portion to be copied. Now there is no reason why the rules of the puzzle itself should not be expressed in such a way as to take account of these markers. If one does express the rules in this way they can be made to be just substitutions. This means to say that the *normal form for puzzles is the substitution type of puzzle.* More definitely we can say:

Given any puzzle we can find a corresponding substitution puzzle *which is equivalent to it in the sense that given a solution of the one we can easily use it to find a solution of the other. If the original puzzle is concerned with rows of pieces of a finite number of different kinds, then the substitutions may be applied as an alternative set of rules to the pieces of the original puzzle. A transformation can be carried out by the rules of the original puzzle if and only if it can be carried out by the substitutions and leads to a final position from which all marker symbols have disappeared.*

This statement is still somewhat lacking in definiteness, and will remain so. I do not propose, for instance, to enter here into the question as to what I mean by the word 'easily'. The statement is moreover one which one does not attempt to prove. Propaganda is more appropriate to it than proof, for its status is something between a theorem and a definition. In so far as we know *a priori* what is a puzzle and what is not, the statement is a theorem. In so far as we do not know what puzzles are, the statement is a definition which tells us something about what they are. One can of course define a puzzle by some phrase beginning, for instance, 'A set of definite rules . . .', but this just throws us back on the definition of 'definite rules'. Equally one can reduce it to the definition of 'computable function' or 'systematic procedure'. A definition of any one of these would define all the rest. Since 1935 a number of definitions have been given, explaining in detail the meaning of one or other of these terms, and these have all been proved equivalent to one another and also equivalent to the above statement. In effect there is no opposition to the view that every puzzle is equivalent to a substitution puzzle.

After these preliminaries let us think again about puzzles as a whole. First let us recapitulate. There are a number of questions to which a puzzle may give rise. When given a particular task one may ask quite simply

(a) *Can this be done?*

Such a straightforward question admits only the straightforward answers, 'Yes' or 'No', or perhaps 'I don't know'. In the case that the answer is 'Yes' the answerer need only have done the puzzle himself beforehand to be sure. If the answer is to be 'No', some rather more subtle kind of argument, more or less mathematical, is necessary. For instance, in the case of the sliding squares one can state that the impossible cases *are* impossible because of the mathematical fact that an odd number of simple interchanges of a number of objects can never bring one back to where one started. One may also be asked

(b) *What is the best way of doing this?*

Such a question does not admit of a straightforward answer. It depends partly on individual differences in people's ideas as to what they find easy. If it is put in the form, 'What is the solution which involves the smallest number of steps?', we again have a straightforward question, but now it is one which is somehow of remarkably little interest. In any particular case where the answer to (a) is 'Yes' one can find the smallest possible number of steps by a tedious and usually impracticable process of enumeration, but the result hardly justifies the labour.

When one has been asked a number of times whether a number of different puzzles of similar nature can be solved one is naturally led to ask oneself

(c) *Is there a systematic procedure by which I can answer these questions, for puzzles of this type?*

If one were feeling rather more ambitious one might even ask

(d) *Is there a systematic procedure by which one can tell whether a puzzle is solvable?*

I hope to show that the answer to this last question is 'No'.

There are in fact certain types of puzzle for which the answer to (c) is 'No'.

Before we can consider this question properly we shall need to be quite clear what we mean by a 'systematic procedure' for deciding a question. But this need not now give us any particular difficulty. A 'systematic procedure' was one of the phrases which we mentioned as being equivalent to the idea of a puzzle, because either could be reduced to the other. If we are now clear as to what a puzzle is, then we should be equally clear about 'systematic procedures'. In fact a systematic procedure is just a puzzle *in which there is never more than one possible move in any of the positions which arise and in which some significance is attached to the final result.*

Now that we have explained the meaning both of the term 'puzzle' and of 'systematic procedure', we are in a position to prove the assertion made in the first paragraph of this article, that there cannot be any systematic procedure for determining whether a puzzle be solvable or not. The proof does not really require the detailed definition of either of the terms, but only the relation between them which we have just explained. Any systematic procedure for deciding whether a puzzle were solvable could certainly be put in the form of a puzzle, with unambiguous moves (i.e. only one move from any one position), and having for its starting position a combination of the rules, the starting position and the final position of the puzzle under investigation.

The puzzle under investigation is also to be described by its rules and starting position. Each of these is to be just a row of symbols. As we are only considering substitution puzzles, the rules need only be a list of all the substitution pairs appropriately punctuated. One possible form of punctuation would be to separate the first member of a pair from the second by an arrow, and to separate the different substitution pairs with colons. In this case the rules

> B may be replaced by BC
> WBW may be deleted

would be represented by ' $: B \rightarrow BC : WBW \rightarrow :$ ' . For the purposes of the argument which follows, however, these arrows and colons are an embarrassment. We shall need the rules to be expressed without the use of any symbols which are barred from appearing in the starting positions. This can be achieved by the following simple, though slightly artificial trick. We first double all the symbols other than the punctuation symbols, thus ': *BB* → *BBCC* : *WWBBWW* → :' . We then replace each arrow by a single symbol, which must be different from those on either side of it, and each colon by three similar symbols, also chosen to avoid clashes. This can always be done if we have at least three symbols available, and the rules above could then be represented as, for instance, '*CCCBBWBBCCBBBWWBBWW BWWW*'. Of course according to these conventions a great variety of different rows of symbols will describe essentially the same puzzle. Quite apart from the arbitrary choice of the punctuating symbols the substitution pairs can be given in any order, and the same pair can be repeated again and again.

Now let $P(R,S)$ stand for 'the puzzle whose rules are described by the row of symbols R and whose starting position is described by S'. Owing to the special form in which we have chosen to describe the rules of puzzles, there is no reason why we should not consider $P(R,R)$ for which the 'rules' also serve as starting position: in fact the success of the argument which follows depends on our doing so. The argument will also be mainly concerned with puzzles in which there is at most one possible move in any position; these may be called 'puzzles with unambiguous moves'. Such a puzzle may be said to have 'come out' if one reaches either the position B or the position W, and the rules do not permit any further moves. Clearly if a puzzle has unambiguous moves it cannot both come out with the end result B and with the end result W.

We now consider the problem of classifying rules R of puzzles into two classes, I and II, as follows:

Class I is to consist of sets R of rules, which represent puzzles with unambiguous moves, and such that $P(R,R)$ comes out with the end result W.

Class II is to include all other cases, i.e. either $P(R,R)$ does not come out, or comes out with the end result B, or else R does not represent a puzzle with unambiguous moves. We may also, if we wish, include in this class sequences of symbols such as *BBBBB* which do not represent a set of rules at all.

Now suppose that, contrary to the theorem that we wish to prove, we have a systematic procedure for deciding whether puzzles come out or not. Then with the aid of this procedure we shall be able to distinguish rules of class I from those of class II. There is no difficulty in deciding whether R really represents a set of rules, and whether they are unambiguous. If there is any difficulty it lies in finding the end result in the cases where the puzzle is known to come out: but this can be decided by actually working the puzzle through. By a principle which has already been explained, this systematic procedure for distinguishing the two classes can itself be put into the form of a substitution puzzle (with rules K, say). When applying these rules K, the rules R of the puzzle under investigation form the starting position, and the end result of the puzzle gives the result of the test. Since the procedure always gives an answer, the puzzle $P(K,R)$ always comes out. The puzzle K might be made to announce its results in a variety of ways, and we may be permitted to suppose that the end result is B for rules R of class I, and W for rules of class II. The opposite choice would be equally possible, and would hold for a slightly different set of rules K', which however we do not choose to favour with our attention. The puzzle with rules K may without difficulty be made to have unambiguous moves. Its essential properties are therefore:

K has unambiguous moves.

$P(K,R)$ always comes out whatever R.

If R is in class I, then $P(K,R)$ has end result B.

If R is in class II, then $P(K,R)$ has end result W.

These properties are however inconsistent with the definitions of the two classes. If we ask ourselves which class K belongs to, we find that neither will do. The puzzle $P(K,K)$ is bound to come out, but the properties of K tell us that we must get end result B if K is in class I and W if it is in class II, whereas the definitions of the classes tell us that the end results must be the other way

round. The assumption that there was a systematic procedure
for telling whether puzzles come out has thus been reduced to
an absurdity.

Thus in connexion with question (c) above we can say that
there are some types of puzzle for which no systematic method
of deciding the question exists. This is often expressed in the
form, 'There is no *decision procedure* for this type of puzzle',
or again, 'The decision problem for this type of puzzle is unsolvable', and so one comes to speak (as in the title of this article)
about 'unsolvable problems' meaning in effect puzzles for which
there is no decision procedure. This is the technical meaning
which the words are now given by mathematical logicians. It
would seem more natural to use the phrase 'unsolvable problem'
to mean just an unsolvable puzzle, as for example 'to transform
1, 2, 3 into 2, 1, 3 by cyclic permutation of the symbols', but
this is not the meaning it now has. However, to minimize confusion I shall here always speak of 'unsolvable decision problems', rather than just 'unsolvable problems', and also speak of
puzzles rather than problems where it is puzzles and not decision
problems that are concerned.

It should be noticed that a decision problem only arises when
one has an infinity of questions to ask. If you ask, 'Is this apple
good to eat?', or 'Is this number prime?', or 'Is this puzzle solvable?' the question can be settled with a single 'Yes' or 'No'.
A finite number of answers will deal with a question about a finite
number of objects, such as the apples in a basket. When the
number is infinite, or in some way not yet completed concerning
say all the apples one may ever be offered, or all whole numbers
or puzzles, a list of answers will not suffice. Some kind of rule
or systematic procedure must be given. Even if the number concerned is finite one may still prefer to have a rule rather than a
list: it may be easier to remember. But there certainly cannot
be an unsolvable decision problem in such cases, because of the
possibility of using finite list.

Regarding decision problems as being concerned with classes
of puzzles, we see that if we have a decision method for one
class it will apply also for any subclass. Likewise, if we have

proved that there is no decision procedure for the subclass, it follows that there is none for the whole class. The most interesting and valuable results about unsolvable decision problems concern the smaller classes of puzzle.

Another point which is worth noticing is quite well illustrated by the puzzle which we considered first of all in which the pieces were sliding squares. If one wants to know whether the puzzle is solvable with a given starting position, one can try moving the pieces about in the hope of reaching the required end-position. If one succeeds, then one will have solved the puzzle and consequently will be able to answer the question, 'Is it solvable?' In the case that the puzzle is solvable one will eventually come on the right set of moves. If one has also a procedure by which, if the puzzle is unsolvable, one would eventually establish the fact that it was so, then one would have a solution of the decision problem for the puzzle. For it is only necessary to apply both processes, a bit of one alternating with a bit of the other, in order eventually to reach a conclusion by one or the other. Actually, in the case of the sliding squares problem, we have got such a procedure, for we know that if, by sliding, one ever reaches the required final position, with squares 14 and 15 interchanged, then the puzzle is impossible.

It is clear then that the difficulty in finding decision procedures for types of puzzle lies in establishing that the puzzle is unsolvable in those cases where it *is* unsolvable. This, as was mentioned on page 16, requires some sort of mathematical argument. This suggests that we might try expressing the statement that the puzzle comes out in a mathematical form and then try and prove it by some systematic process. There is no particular difficulty in the first part of this project, the mathematical expression of the statement about the puzzle. But the second half of the project is bound to fail, because by a famous theorem of Gödel no systematic method of proving mathematical theorems is sufficiently complete to settle every mathematical question, yes or no. In any case we are now in a position to give an independent proof of this. If there were such a systematic method of proving mathematical theorems we could apply it to our puzzles and for each one eventually either prove that it was solvable or unsolvable; this would provide a systematic method of determining whether the puzzle was solvable or not, contrary to what we have already proved.

This result about the decision problem for puzzles, or, more accurately speaking, a number of others very similar to it, was proved in 1936–7. Since then a considerable number of further decision problems have been shown to be unsolvable. They are all proved to be unsolvable by showing that if they were solvable one could use the solution to provide a solution of the original one. They could all without difficulty be reduced to the same unsolvable problem. A number of these results are mentioned very shortly below. No attempt is made to explain the technical terms used, as most readers will be familiar with some of them, and the space required for the explanation would be quite out of proportion to its usefulness in this context.

(1) It is not possible to solve the decision problem even for substitution processes applied to rows of black and white counters only.

(2) There are certain particular puzzles for which there is no decision procedure, the rules being fixed and the only variable element being the starting position.

(3) There is no procedure for deciding whether a given set of axioms leads to a contradiction or not.

(4) The 'word problem in semi-groups with cancellation' is not solvable.

(5) It has recently been announced from Russia that the 'word problem in groups' is not solvable. This is a decision problem not unlike the 'word problem in semi-groups', but very much more important, having applications in topology: attempts were being made to solve this decision problem before any such problems had been proved unsolvable. No adequately complete proof is yet available, but if it is correct this is a considerable step forward.

(6) There is a set of 102 matrices of order 4, with integral coefficients such that there is no decision method for determining

whether another given matrix is or is not expressible as a product of matrices from the given set.

These are, of course, only a selection from the results. Although quite a number of decision problems are now known to be unsolvable, we are still very far from being in a position to say of a given decision problem, whether it is solvable or not. Indeed, we shall never be quite in that position, for the question whether a given decision problem is solvable is itself one of the undecidable decision problems. The results which have been found are on the whole ones which have fallen into our laps rather than ones which have positively been searched for. Considerable efforts have however been made over the word problem in groups (see (5) above). Another problem which mathematicians are very anxious to settle is known as 'the decision problem of the equivalence of manifolds'. This is something like one of the problems we have already mentioned, that concerning the twisted wire puzzles. But whereas with the twisted wire puzzles the pieces are quite rigid, the 'equivalence of manifolds' problem concerns pieces which one is allowed to bend, stretch, twist, or compress as much as one likes, without ever actually breaking them or making new junctions or filling in holes. Given a number of interlacing pieces of plasticine one may be asked to transform them in this way into another given form. The decision problem for this class of problem is the 'decision problem for the equivalence of manifolds'. It is probably unsolvable, but has never been proved to be so. A similar decision problem which might well be unsolvable is the one concerning knots which has already been mentioned.

The results which have been described in this article are mainly of a negative character, setting certain bounds to what we can hope to achieve purely by reasoning. These, and some other results of mathematical logic may be regarded as going some way towards a demonstration, within mathematics itself, of the inadequacy of 'reason' unsupported by common sense.

FURTHER READING

Kleene, S. C. *Introduction to Metamathematics*, Amsterdam, 1952.

WHY CHEMICAL ENGINEERING?

J. F. PEARSON

ONE answer to the question posed above is to glance rapidly at some pictures. Inset 2 shows the use for industrial production of equipment which, in form, material, and even in size, was essentially of laboratory type. The date of this picture is 1820. Inset 3 shows a bench of early petroleum stills. Such a design was obtained by taking the methods and apparatus of the laboratory chemist and handing them to mechanical and civil engineers for enlargement to industrial scale. Each of these stills held some thousands of gallons of oil. Inset 4 – and also Inset 1 and 7 – show the change which results when the carrying out of chemical operations efficiently and on a large scale is approached as a problem in its own right, that, by chemical engineers.

More systematically, we may begin by considering briefly the nature of engineering, and how its subdivision into branches has arisen; and, from the industrial background of chemical engineering, proceed to a single example of a complete chemical process. This will give us the background necessary to appreciate what are the usual stages in adapting a laboratory process to large-scale production. By this time, the original question may be presumed to have already been answered, and we can proceed to the scientific approach made by the chemical engineer to some of the more important aspects of his work, and the requirements and value of training for it.

The word 'engineer' has broadened in significance since its original use as meaning a person who made or operated engines, until now it may denote anyone connected with the technological details of harnessing natural sources of energy, and diverting them to useful ends. We shall be concerned here with the function of engineers (or, to use another term, applied scientists) at a professional level. We imagine an engineer to be responsible for the design, manufacture, and erection of some kind of equipment or structure, and this is often regarded as the feature which distinguishes his province from that of an applied scientist. But as the various facets of industrial technology have developed, this distinction has become increasingly nebulous, and it will not be emphasized.

Conventional history tells us that engineers were at one time either 'military' or 'civil'. During the last hundred years, specialization, occasioned by gradually increasing wealth of knowledge and experience, has resulted in the creation of new branches of engineering. Frequently each branch is built up round a particular kind of engineering appliance designed for a specific purpose; hence the existence of automobile, marine, and aeronautical engineering. Sometimes also the application of knowledge of a certain sort of physical phenomena may give rise to separate branches of engineering, for example electrical engineering. Yet there is an underlying unity of thought which every type of engineer has in common, and which guides his mental approach to the everyday problems of engineering practice.

This conformity results largely from the fact that engineers are invariably concerned with unique problems to which an answer of some kind must be found; for example, a bridge has to be designed for a particular river, to withstand a definite loading, or an engine to develop a certain power, when its weight and cost are kept below fixed limits. The selection of the problem is generally outside the control of the engineer, but in its solution he can use whatever methods and knowledge he pleases (science, mathematics, instinct, experience, economics, etc.). Although nowadays the engineer makes a growing use of physical science, his outlook is nevertheless substantially different from that of the pure scientist, who enjoys freedom of investigation over a wide field, poses his own problems in any part of that field, and is bound by economic considerations only as to the means used to solve them, not in his solutions as such. If the scientist's choice of problem proves wrong, he is free to modify his original statement of the problem, or, if necessary, to turn to an entirely new section of his field. The engineer has not this freedom; he must always find a solution, however inadequate on occasions, to the problem as stated. He is concerned always with the particular rather than the general; he must concentrate all his resources on a single problem, the solution to which is all-important, irrespective of the intrinsic merits of the *method* of solution.

While the various branches of engineering have arisen fortuitously and the special problems with which they deal have often been tackled in an empirical fashion, the pressure of economic competition in modern industry calls often for a higher standard of efficiency, based on greater insight, when new products and processes are introduced. Advancing scientific knowledge has, in fact, begun to place more powerful methods at the disposal of the engineer, but to make the fullest use of them he must frequently look beyond the confines of his own particular branch. Obvious instances, involving electron physics and combustion theory respectively, are those of the electrical engineer who uses electronic methods for controlling rotating machinery and of the automobile engineer who decides to investigate an improved fuel for internal combustion engines. The contemporary engineer who wishes to be in the forefront of progress should possess a background of fundamental ideas based on scientific principles, as well as a detailed knowledge of his peculiar technology. The principles in question are, in the main, those commonly (but inadequately) referred to as 'nineteenth century physics', though the chemical engineer looks on them in a different light from the physicist, being interested only in their application to his special problems. Different fields of engineering vary in the scope that they offer for using scientific methods, and it is one object of this article to show how wide a range of physical science lies within the scope of chemical engineering.

The development of chemical engineering as a profession has happened concurrently with expansion in the chemical industry during the last fifty or sixty years. In the years before 1914, the predominant chemical industry was built up in Germany, whose achievements in the fields of dyestuffs, synthetic nitrates, and coal hydrogenation were the work of chemists collaborating with mechanical and civil engineers. Consequently German chemical plant of that time, and even of a later period, tended to take a similar form to the chemical laboratory apparatus used in research, except for an increase in size. (This is the point, mentioned at the beginning, which it has been sought to make in pictures.) During the same period, the foundations of the new profession were laid in the United States, a major part in the educational field being played by the Massachusetts Institute of Technology, whose president, A. D. Little, was one of the first to introduce the idea of 'unit operations' – to which we shall return later – and the application of this to plant design.

During the period between the two world wars, the profession developed rapidly in the United States, owing largely to increasing competition for world markets, and the ensuing need for more efficient methods in the chemical industry. Another stimulating factor was the demand for chemical engineers created by the growth of the petroleum refining industry, and the introduction of chemical products derived from the crude petroleum of American oil fields. At the present time, the United States is rightly regarded as the principal world centre of chemical engineering training and research.

England possessed one of the pioneers of the new profession in G. E. Davis, who recognized the need for more systematic methods of chemical plant design late in the nineteenth century, and published his *Handbook of Chemical Engineering* in 1901. After the first world war, however, despite the formation of an Institution of Chemical Engineers in 1922, this country has failed to keep pace with the American development of chemical engineering, and, in particular, the output of university graduates qualified in the subject has been low.

THE CHEMICAL ENGINEER IN INDUSTRY

The chemical industry is dependent for its existence on the production at a competitive cost of chemical products for which there is a demand, either for bulk industrial use or from small individual consumers. Conditions in the industry are far from static, and new products, with actual or potential markets, are developed in the laboratory by chemists and other workers in natural science, who are employed in industrial organizations. As a result of his researches, the pure scientist establishes the conditions required to bring about, on a small scale, the physical and chemical phenomena involved in making the proposed new product. The function of the engineer is then to consider the results obtained by the laboratory scientist, with whom he is often in close personal contact, and to visualize what will happen when the same product, with accompanying phenomena, is obtained on a much larger scale. The primary problem of the chemical engineer is thus one of 'scale-up'. And his primary justification is the difference in methods, approach, and background knowledge which the process of 'scale-up' requires.

After he has imagined a production process on an industrial scale, and set down on paper his conclusions, both qualitative and quantitative, the chemical engineer often passes on the resulting information to other workers—for example, mechanical and civil engineers, draughtsmen, architects, and so on – for the completion of detailed plant design. Hence the profession of chemical engineering supplies a link in the chain joining pure scientific research to a saleable commodity, and it is naturally desirable that a chemical engineer should have some familiarity with the other links in the chain; that is, his interests should embrace chemistry, mechanical and civil engineering, and even architecture and economics. For this reason, it is sometimes stated that a chemical engineer is a 'jack of all trades', and possibly even a master of none. He has in any case his special province: the qualitative and quantitative analysis of large-scale chemical phenomena.

It follows that chemical engineering principles find application in any industry which, though not producing chemicals, makes use of chemical change. Examples which suggest themselves are iron and steel production, the carbonization of coal, atomic power generation, ceramics, and the pulp and paper industries. Although a chemical engineer working in such an industry might never be asked to carry out a complete plant design, his knowledge would be invaluable, particularly in the development of new ideas and procedures.

Because the chemical industry is expanding rapidly, the initiation and design of new processes for manufacturing new products has been emphasized, though perhaps not unduly. In addition, the chemical engineer can, and does, make significant contributions in other ways, such as the investigations of faults in operating plant ('trouble-shooting'), or by experimental work on semi-scale ('pilot') plant set up as a trial step during the development of a new process. Alternatively, he may engage in the management, or engineering maintenance, of a production plant or of a factory manufacturing chemicals. In these latter functions, however, he inevitably loses something of his identity as an engineer, and design may be considered the finest flowering of the practice of chemical engineering.

THE COMPLETE CHEMICAL PROCESS

We shall now describe in more detail some characteristics of an industrial chemical process, in order to emphasize the peculiarities of the chemical engineering outlook. Until recent years, it was customary to assume that large-scale chemical processes could be subdivided, for purposes of analysis, into a number of operations, according to the kinds of industrial equipment in which the reactions, and ancillary treatments and separations, were carried out. Thus the chemical engineer thought in terms of 'unit operations', as they are called, such as distillation, evaporation, mixing, and grinding. The separate study of individual operations, from combinations of which all chemical production plants are made up, led to the development of generalized methods of considerable value for the design of equipment.

While the idea of a 'unit operation' is still retained because it leads to a useful system of classification, the modern tendency is to concentrate on the more basic features which most unit operations have in common, in an effort to evolve design procedures of still greater generality and power.

To make the relevant ideas more concrete, let us consider the steps in the design of a complete chemical process for the production of phenol, a white solid compound with a variety of uses, particularly for pharmaceutical purposes, and as an intermediate during the manufacture of dyestuffs. The raw material is coal tar, from which benzene is separated by distillation, and then chlorinated to produce chlorobenzene. For simplicity, we shall assume that a supply of chlorobenzene is already available, and that a plant is required for its conversion to phenol by 'hydrolysis', in which the chlorine atom is replaced by the hydroxyl group, $-OH$. The chlorobenzene, which is a colourless liquid boiling at about 132° C., may be hydrolysed in a number of ways, of which the commonest, in industrial practice, is heating with aqueous sodium hydroxide:

$$C_6H_5Cl + NaOH \longrightarrow C_6H_5OH + NaCl$$
$$\text{(chlorobenzene)} \qquad \text{(phenol)}$$

Subsidiary reactions also occur, causing the formation of small quantities of other products, such as diphenyl $(C_6H_5.C_6H_5)$. The above reaction has been the subject of extensive laboratory investigation, particularly in the United States, and much of the resulting data published. If this information were not available, a laboratory research programme would be carried out by a chemist in order to determine the physical conditions (temperature, pressure, concentration, etc.) required to produce different percentage yields of product, and also to measure the reaction rate. For purposes of comparison, the same information may be obtained about a number of alternative reactions for converting chlorobenzene to phenol, for example by reaction with water vapour in the gaseous state:

$$C_6H_5Cl + H_2O \longrightarrow C_6H_5OH + HCl$$

In addition, when the information cannot be found in the published literature, the chemist will establish values for the physical properties (such as melting point, boiling point, density, and viscosity) of the appropriate chemicals, and make experimental determinations of the equilibrium concentrations of the reactants and products at varying degrees of dilution with water. Such data are valuable, or essential, at a later stage of the project; for instance, equilibrium data for the mixture containing the product are required since, after cooling, it separates into two liquid layers, each of which can be run off to separate partially the phenol from the other compounds present.

At this point, the work of the chemist (unless he is also something of a chemical engineer) is, in a sense, finished, and the chemical engineer can use the information already obtained for calculations during design of the full-size plant. For the reaction producing phenol from chlorobenzene and sodium hydroxide, laboratory data, obtained from a small steel reaction vessel, or 'autoclave', indicate optimum conditions of about 300° C. temperature, 4,000 pounds per square inch pressure, and 10 per cent sodium hydroxide concentration. The reaction rate appears to be independent of the sodium hydroxide concentration, and to be proportional directly to the chlorobenzene concentration, so that it is an example of a 'first order' reaction.*

When the same chemical reaction is carried out on an industrial scale, it will be the means of producing perhaps five tons of phenol a day. The central feature of the plant will be the reaction vessel, operating continuously, with a steady flow of partially vaporized liquid through it, in contrast to the small laboratory reactor, which contained a static batch of reacting mixture. Through the continuous reactor passes a turbulent two-phase mixture, in which the various kinds of molecules are moving to and fro under the combined influence of temperature and pressure gradients, while some are being removed and others created owing to chemical action. Most of these phenomena the chemist was inclined to take for granted, and just to measure the over-all

*A first-order reaction is one of which the rate is determined by the concentration of only one constituent and is directly proportional to this concentration. See, for example, 'Mechanisms of Chemical Change' by K. D. Wadsworth in *Science News 26*.

Production of Phenol from Chlorobenzene

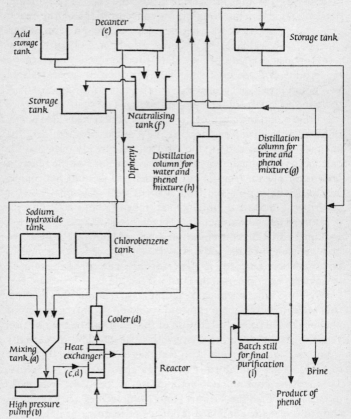

Fig. 1. Simplified diagram of a process plant for the production of phenol from chlorobenzene. As well as the main reaction vessel (*bottom centre*), equipment is required for the following operations: (*a*) Mixing and emulsifying of chlorobenzene, sodium hydroxide, and re-circulated diphenyl, (*b*) high-pressure pumping of the resulting mixture, (*c*) pre-heating of the mixed reactants by hot products from the reaction vessel, (*d*) cooling of the product mixture after it leaves the reaction vessel, (*e*) decanting of the

yield of product, but the chemical engineer must pay a greater attention to detail if his design is to have the maximum chance of commercial success. For economic reasons, if for no other, he must be able to analyse as quantitatively as possible the complex state of affairs in the reactor in order to make a reasonably accurate prediction of the necessary size of equipment for production of the desired concentration of phenol, and to estimate the energy required both to heat the flowing mixture and to pump it through the reaction vessel.

As well as the reactor, any process plant also includes equipment for various auxiliary operations, such as preparation of reactants in the appropriate concentrations and at the necessary temperature, and separation of the product mixture into its constituents after it leaves the reactor. Indeed, the majority of the so-called unit operations are separations of this nature. It is convenient to distinguish clearly between unit (physical) 'operations' and unit (chemical) 'processes', or types of reaction. Figure 1 shows a simplified arrangement of a complete plant for the conversion of chlorobenzene to phenol. Here there is only one 'unit process' – hydrolysis – but nine 'unit operations' are performed (see caption).

CHEMICAL ENGINEERING DESIGN

Figure 2 shows diagrammatically a simplified version of the stages involved in adapting a laboratory process to large-scale production. The darker lines distinguish functions which are primarily the concern of the chemical engineer, although natur-

---

liquid product mixture to remove diphenyl, which sinks to the bottom and is run off, (*f*) addition of hydrochloric acid to neutralize the caustic mixture, which then forms two layers, (*g*) separation of the lower layer (mainly brine and phenol) into its components by distillation, (*h*) separation of the upper layer (mainly water and phenol) into its components by distillation, and (*i*) further purification of the phenol by another distillation. The letters (*a*), (*b*), etc. in the diagram correspond with the operations here listed.

ally the number of such steps will depend largely on the size of the organization undertaking the work; in a small firm one individual may be responsible for the whole project from the results of laboratory research to plant erection.

The first step is the preparation of a flow-sheet, or balance of materials and energy quantities flowing in and out of every part of the suggested process. It may not be possible to make a clear-cut decision as to the types of equipment required in the plant, but at least the kind of operations which will be used are not usually in doubt.

When the flow-sheet is completed, the individual unit operations and processes which will make up the entire plant are considered. Three groups of unit operations exist, concerned respectively with size reduction, mixing, and physical separation of materials. Size reduction involves crushing and grinding of solids, while mixing refers to blending of liquids and pastes, which may, or may not, contain suspended solids. In Table I (on page 36) a number of examples of common unit operations of the third, and most important, group are classified according to the phase or phases (solid, liquid, or gas) taking part in the separation.

As a result of experience and experiment during the last half-century, quantitative methods have been developed for calculation of the performance of equipment used for carrying out unit operations, but it must be admitted that at the present time such methods are often of a semi-empirical nature, and a great deal of scope for fundamental investigation remains.

Stages in a chemical plant which involve chemical reaction can, to some extent, be systematically treated according to the nature of the reaction. As yet, however, the classification and analysis of various types of reaction, or 'unit processes',* have not been developed to the same extent as in the case of unit operations. It is generally true that, while a particular kind of equipment is reserved for a certain unit operation, several unit processes may be carried out in one kind of equipment, so that,

*Typical unit processes are: hydrolysis, sulphonation, esterification, nitration, fermentation, hydrogenation, polymerization.

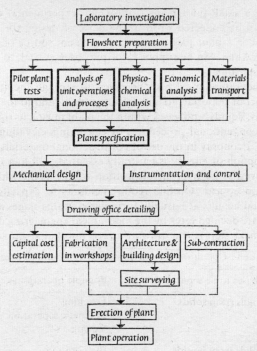

Fig. 2. Stages in the design of a chemical plant. Those in darker lines are normally performed by the chemical engineer.

from a practical viewpoint, the idea of a unit process does not provide so convenient a grouping as that of a unit operation.

A preliminary analysis of the probable cost of the plant and the selling price of the product is carried out after preparation of the flow-sheet, in order to determine marketing potentialities, and to decide whether or not to continue with the project.

The methods of physical chemistry (including thermodynamics, reaction kinetics, and electrochemistry) are of great value in elucidating the phenomena involved, and in providing data for calculations. In some cases, where the process is new, or data are difficult to obtain, it may be desirable to erect and operate a small pilot plant from which experimental observations can be collected to form the basis of design for a larger plant; such a pilot plant is also a convenient source of product samples which can be supplied, for purposes of trial, to possible future consumers.

Consideration must also be given to storage facilities, and transport of materials to and from the plant, and to the moving of solids, liquids, and gases within the plant during its operation, by the conventional procedures of conveying, elevating, pumping, etc. Economy in the use of constructional materials and the consumption of energy is naturally essential, and to a large extent governs the over-all disposition of the plant which now begins to appear. Outline requirements as to capacities, flow rates, and heights are usually formulated at this stage, while the details are decided later by the mechanical engineering designer.

The next step is the drawing up of an equipment schedule,

TABLE I: *Operations for the Physical Separation of Materials*

Phases to be separated	Possible operations
Solids from solids	Leaching Magnetic separation Sieving
Solids from liquids	Evaporation Drying Filtration
Solids from gases	Dust filtration Electrostatic precipitation
Liquids from liquids	Distillation Solvent extraction Centrifuging
Liquids from gases	Settling Gas washing
Gases from gases	Adsorption on to solids Absorption in liquids Fractional condensation

including the essential details as to capacities, sizes, and materials of construction, with the appropriate gas, water, electricity and steam services. This information may then be passed on to mechanical and civil design engineers for more extensive detailing in a drawing office. The remaining steps, including workshop construction and plant erection, are self-explanatory. An important feature of most modern chemical plants, which is considered at an early stage in design, is the provision of instruments for measurement and automatic control of physical variables, such as temperature, pressure, and humidity, during the plant operation.

SCIENTIFIC ASPECTS OF CHEMICAL ENGINEERING

Let us now consider the scientific approach made by the chemical engineer to some of the more important aspects of this work. As indicated in the above discussion of a phenol plant, the cardinal task of the chemical engineer is the quantitative analysis of various phenomena which involve interchange of matter and energy. He can do a great deal towards accomplishing this by deduction from his knowledge of scientific fundamentals. Consequently, he relies less on experiment and *a posteriori* conclusions than does the pure scientist; naturally a full-scale chemical plant cannot be erected to decide its possibilities, for the same reason that a bridge cannot be built to decide if it will be strong enough.

For analysis, it is convenient to classify the relevant phenomena in two main groups:

(*a*) *Dynamic phenomena,* involving the transfer of matter by diffusion, eddying, or bulk flowing; the removal and introduction of matter by chemical reaction; and the transfer of heat. The necessary calculations are often simplified by the existence of 'steady-state' conditions which will therefore be separately discussed. So also will be the use of dimensional methods for the analysis of transfer phenomena.

(*b*) *Static phenomena* at a state of equilibrium, without net transfer of matter or energy.

Sometimes several of these phenomena occur simultaneously

in one part of a chemical plant; for example, in the phenol reaction vessel, matter interchanges take place owing to chemical
reaction, diffusion, and eddying, also heat is supplied to the
reacting mass, which itself gives out a small quantity of heat as
a consequence of the reaction. The mixture in the phenol reactor
is maintained in the liquid state owing to the high pressure, but
in many other cases of frequent occurrence in chemical plant
more than one physical phase is present, transfer and equilibrium between phases being a problem of paramount importance.

Dynamic phenomena

Most of the basic scientific theories used by chemical engineers derive from classical physics. During dynamic phenomena,
the rate of transfer, Q, is normally proportional to a driving
force, F, and inversely proportional to a resistance, R, so that
an equation of the following form may be written:

$$Q = kF/R$$

A familiar transfer process giving rise to such an equation is the
flow of an electric current, which obeys Ohm's law, F being the
electromotive force, and R the electrical resistance. The value of
the constant, k, has to be determined from experiment, and the
units of measurement are usually such that $k = 1$.

For the other types of transfer processes, a quantity, K, known
as a transfer coefficient, and numerically equal to the reciprocal
of the resistance, is normally used in place of the resistance itself.
Since the transfer rate depends on the cross-sectional area (perpendicular to the direction of flow) which is considered, it is
convenient to evaluate transfer coefficients per unit area. The
driving forces causing transfer from one part of a medium to
another, for the three cases of transfer of heat (in solids and
fluids), diffusional transfer of matter in gases, and in liquids, are
the respective differences in temperature (T), pressure (P), and
concentration (C), measured between any two points in the
medium concerned. Thus, using the symbol A to denote cross-
sectional area, the equations for these three phenomena, giving
the rate of transfer between the two points considered, are:

$$Q_1 = K_1 A_1 T$$
$$Q_2 = K_2 A_2 P$$
$$Q_3 = K_3 A_3 C$$

Equations of this nature are the basis on which most transfer calculations are carried out. In practice, the geometrical configuration of the equipment, and the fact that several such phenomena may be occurring simultaneously, can make this simple theory exceedingly difficult to apply, or at least result in some complicated mathematics. It is interesting to note that the driving force operating in the case of any particular transfer process is decided from experience or experiment. Indeed, it is an open question as to whether or not concentration-difference is an accurate measure of the driving force for matter transfer by diffusion in liquids. Nothing about the intrinsic character of the transfer mechanisms is revealed by the above rules, and an analysis based on first principles exists only for gases, for which Maxwell's kinetic theory leads to similar relations for the transfer of heat and matter.

The numerical values of the various transfer coefficients can be measured directly, and tabulated, for the transfer of heat and matter within solids, where the problem is not complicated, as it is for transfer in fluids, by freedom of molecular movement, and by the existence of an enormous range of mixtures of differing composition and transfer properties. For diffusion in gases, the kinetic theory leads to an expression for the appropriate transfer coefficient. For diffusion in liquids, less direct methods must be used for estimation of the K values from the physical properties of the mixture under consideration.

Once the transfer coefficient has been found, the final step in engineering calculation is to determine the cross-sectional area, A, which is required to maintain the desired rate of flow, Q. This is given by the relation:

$$A = Q / K \ x \ (\text{driving force})$$

According to this numerical value of A, the size or capacity of the proposed equipment is chosen, and the primary part of the chemical engineer's work is complete.

As well as diffusional transfer, caused by kinetic movement of molecules, transfer of matter and energy in fluids often takes place as a result of bulk motion, or eddying, during which lumps of fluid, of much larger than molecular size, move coherently under the influence of concentration differences. Only a rudimentary physical theory, suggested by Osborne Reynolds, and developed by L. Prandtl and Th. von Kármán, exists as a basis for analysis of this sort of transfer phenomenon. The theory employs an analogy between molecular motion of gas molecules and the bulk movement of eddying fluid masses, and hinges largely on the definition of a quantity known as the 'mixing length', which plays a part in this theory of eddying similar to the 'mean free path', or mean distance between molecular collisions, in the kinetic theory of gases.

Changes in the spatial distribution of matter may also be caused by chemical reactions between the molecules of a mixture, and the rate of reaction is dependent on both the concentrations of the reactants and the number of different kinds of molecules which take part. The determination of quantitative relations for reaction rates is, however, still largely empirical, and no comprehensive method of analysis exists, except for simple cases, so that direct resort to experiment is often necessary.

A notable exception to the generalized transfer law described above is energy transfer by thermal radiation. For radiation from one surface at a high temperature to another at a much lower temperature, however, the same relation (transfer rate = driving force × transfer coefficient) is approximately true, the transfer coefficient being proportional to the cube of the higher temperature.

Steady-state transfer

A circumstance which often simplifies transfer calculations is the existence of many items of chemical plant which operate steadily, so that while the composition, pressure, temperature, and other properties vary at different positions in the equipment concerned, those same quantities are independent of time. In order to assign a physical meaning to the driving force, transfer is presumed to occur only across certain limited regions, or films, in the fluid mixture, which is tantamount to supposing all the transfer resistance to be concentrated in such films. In fact, most of the transfer resistance generally exists near a fluid boundary of some kind, either at the containing wall of the vessel, or at an interface between two phases, so that films may be postulated to occur at, or near, these boundaries. To clarify this idea, let us take an example of an interchanger used for transferring heat from a hot gas to a liquid; a case in point is the pre-heater for the mixed chlorobenzene and sodium hydroxide in the phenol manufacturing plant. The liquid to be heated is pumped through one or more tubes, and the hot gas flows in the annular space outside the tubes, in the opposite direction to the liquid, as shown in Figure 3. There is a gradual fall in gas temperature and rise in liquid temperature as each passes through the interchanger, so that at any point along a tube length, if the operation is carried out with steady rates of flow, there will be a constant difference between the average gas temperature and the average liquid temperature at that point. As a consequence of the inherent nature of the flow, most of the resistance to heat transmission is concentrated in films on either side of the tube wall, where, owing to the calming effect of this stationary boundary, transfer is predominantly by molecular diffusion rather than by eddying. Thus most of the temperature drop between the gas and liquid at any given point along the length of the tube occurs across these films, as might be expected from the analogous flow problem of a series electrical circuit in which the electromotive force across any section is proportional to the resistance of that section. Figure 3 shows the decrease in average gas temperature along the length of the interchanger from T_i at inlet to T_o at outlet, and also the increase in average liquid temperature from t_i to t_o. Since the temperature differences are largely confined to the films, the main bodies of gas and liquid at any point along the interchanger are assumed to be at average uniform temperatures of t_1 and t_2 respectively, so that the driving force for heat transmission perpendicular to the tube wall is $(t_1 - t_2)$. If the heat transfer coefficient, K, is estimated, either from a knowledge of the film thicknesses, or by calculation from known physical characteristics of the flowing fluids, then the surface area of the tube, and hence the appropriate size of heat interchanger for any given rate of heat exchange, Q, may be determined from our general formula:

$$A = Q/K(t_1 - t_2)$$

In practice K and $(t_1 - t_2)$ vary along the length of the tube, and mean values are normally used.

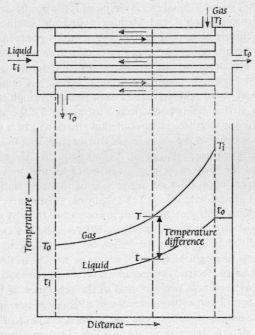

Fig. 3. Diagram of a counter-flow heat interchanger (*above*) with a temperature-distribution graph (*below*) for the gas and liquid streams.

Matter transfer is treated in a similar way to the above heat-transfer problem, and when transfer of both heat and matter occurs simultaneously, the two phenomena are sometimes assumed to be superimposed. Recent study of such multi-transfer systems, by L. Onsager and others, has led to an important extension of thermodynamic theory.

Dimensional methods

The procedure of dimensional analysis, although it does not spring from any real understanding of the phenomena, has nevertheless considerable power to solve transfer and other chemical engineering problems. Provided the variables which influence the phenomenon concerned can be picked out, then any relation between them can be formulated as an equation, either side of which has the same physical dimensions (expressible, for example, in terms of mass, length, and time). This principle of dimensional homogeneity, as it is called, amounts to the statement that it would be nonsense to write, on one side of an equation, the mass of a tender full of coal, and, on the other, the speed of a train, and then to relate these two quantities directly; they have different dimensions and cannot be equated. On the other hand, if a number of further factors were introduced – for example, the distance which the train was required to run before refuelling, and the dependence of air-resistance on speed which would affect its consumption of coal – then a possible relation could be found.

The further application of this principle leads to relations involving 'dimensionless groups', each of which contains an arrangement of some of the relevant quantities in the form of a ratio with dimensions of unity. A classical example of such a group is the celebrated 'Reynolds number' (written Re), which occurs in the analysis of fluid flow, and equals $ud\zeta/\mu$, where u represents the velocity, d the 'characteristic length', ζ the density, and μ the viscosity of the fluid. Expressions can also be deduced by dimensional analysis for the various transfer coefficients. For instance, the heat transfer coefficient, K_1, is found to depend on the two following dimensionless groups: $K_1 d/k$, called the 'Nusselt number', where k is the thermal conductivity of the fluid concerned; and $C_p \mu/k$, the 'Prandtl number', where C_p is the specific heat of the fluid.

The Nusselt (*Nu*), Prandtl (*Pr*), and Reynolds numbers are related, and the form of this relation can be determined by experiment. For heat transfer between fluids flowing in cylindrical tubes, the transfer coefficient for one of the film resistances may be obtained from the equation:

$$Nu = 0.023 \, Re^{0.8} \, Pr^{0.4}$$

This equation is valid for all fluids and flow conditions, irrespective of variations in physical properties, and from it a value of *K* for the film resistance may be calculated. The resistances (i.e. the reciprocals of the transfer coefficients, *K*) of the films on each side of the tube wall may be added to the resistance of the wall itself to give an 'over-all' resistance from one fluid to the other.

If a complete analysis of transfer phenomena, based on fundamentals, existed, it would be expected to yield equations between the variables of similar form to those found by dimensional reasoning. Analogous expressions to the above can be developed for matter transfer in fluids as a result of differences in concentration.

Static phenomena

Many of the phenomena occurring in the chemical industry are at, or near, a stationary state of equilibrium, when the physical quantities characterizing the system remain invariable with time. In such a case, the chemical engineer is frequently enabled to predict the conditions necessary for carrying out processes by means of the classical and statistical methods of thermodynamics, developed in the first instance by physicists and physical chemists. The essential assumption of thermodynamics is that a state of equilibrium exists, or is 'nearly enough' approached. Its use leads to the discovery of relations between different physical properties, some of which can be easily measured by direct experiment, while others cannot. For such relations to be of value to the engineer there must be available numerical values of relevant properties of single substances and mixtures under various equilibrium conditions. Thermodynamic methods are then of great value both for the estimation of related properties, for which experimental values are not available, and also for checking the consistency of experimental observations of different properties. Equilibrium situations are diverse in character, and a few of the more common situations which give rise to them will now be mentioned briefly.

A number of chemical reactions of industrial importance are reversible, and proceed in either direction, reaching a dynamic equilibrium when the forward and backward reaction rates become equal.

Chemical plant operations, particularly separation processes, are often carried out in a series of stages, each stage being approximately at equilibrium. A good example is the use of continuous fractional distillation to separate a mixture of liquids (e.g. phenol and water) into its components. The distillation can be performed in a vertical cylindrical vessel, or column, containing circular diaphragms, or plates, at equal spacings along its length. The liquid mixture is fed on to a predetermined plate in the column and during operation liquid flows downward from one plate to another, while vapour rises up the column. There is a stepwise variation of liquid and vapour composition between plates, so that any single plate contains a liquid mixture, with a vapour space between it and the next higher plate. For purpose of calculation, the liquid and vapour at any plate are assumed to be in a state of equilibrium. Other separations where similar kinds of stage-wise equilibria occur are gas absorption in liquids, extraction of solid mixtures by liquid solvents, and evaporation of solutions.

Another common type of problem in which equilibrium conditions can usefully be assumed involves phenomena near a boundary between phases. For example, the quantity of gas adsorbed on a solid surface can be determined from the thermodynamic considerations on the assumption that a state of equilibrium exists, although the *rate* of such adsorption is a dynamic problem. Again, the formation and stability of systems containing small particles of one phase, such as dusts, solid crystals, suspended droplets, and colloidal particles are of outstanding interest in chemical engineering.

Finally, the equilibrium states associated with electrochemical reactions have also been tackled extensively by thermodynamics.

CHEMICAL ENGINEERING EDUCATION

Since the second world war there has been, in Great Britain, some resurgence of interest in chemical engineering, and several small schools for its teaching now exist. Nevertheless, the number of qualified chemical engineers practising in Britain, expressed as a percentage of the total number of professionally qualified engineers, is still small compared with that in the United States.

The chemical industry employs people with widely different kinds of knowledge and experience. An academic study of chemical engineering, however, is generally (and correctly) confined to the application of scientific principles, not because other aspects, such as production planning, economics, etc., are considered unimportant, but rather because to make the most use of the time available academic bodies concentrate on the sort of knowledge they can best impart.

Comparison of formal courses of study at university level in chemical engineering with those in the older academic disciplines of chemistry, physics, and engineering leads to three principal conclusions. Firstly, since chemical engineering presents particular methods of attacking problems, for which an extensive factual background is not essential, it places a greater emphasis on a student's power of reasoning and logical analysis, and less on his memory, than does a study of chemistry, or even physics. Secondly, as the prime objective always in view during the study of chemical engineering is operation of industrial processes, the practical needs of society may be stressed to better advantage than perhaps is the case in the study of pure science. Thirdly, compared with other branches of engineering, chemical engineering offers a wider choice of specific problems for study, since chemical, as well as physical, phenomena may be involved.

Thus there seems adequate justification for regarding chemical engineering as a valuable educational field. One danger, however, is the possibility that a chemical engineering course may become too diffuse because it attempts to cover too wide a field, rather than concentrating on scientific principles, and applying them to a small number of well-chosen examples from industrial practice. For comparison, it may be noted that this article has consisted essentially of one main example, with such illustrations of principle as were relevant to it, and that many other possible topics have been therefore omitted. It is the essence of chemical engineering that applications of its principles can be made in the entire range of chemical industries: this fact may easily be lost sight of by introducing an excessive wealth of technical detail at the expense of an adequate scientific background for the student.

FURTHER READING

A number of previous issues of *Science News* contain articles of chemical engineering interest. The first four of the following are mainly descriptive accounts of chemical production processes; the others are on relevant scientific topics. Issues not in print are starred.

Taylor, F. Sherwood. 'A Century of British Chemistry'. *SN 5.*

Smith, E. L., and Crammer, J. L. 'Making Penicillin'. *SN 6.*

Moncrieff, R. W. 'Synthetic Fibres'. *SN 14.**

Gilbert, C. G. 'Making Chemicals from Petroleum'. *SN 16.**

Sutton, O. G. 'The Restless Wind'. *SN 11.**

Standing, B. 'Hydraulic Models'. *SN 17.**

Burton, W. K. 'Theory of Crystal Growth'. *SN 21.*

Wadsworth, K. D. 'Mechanisms of Chemical Change'. *SN 26.*

Davies, R. O. 'Irreversible Thermodynamics'. *SN 28.*

Standard technical works, with a reasonably modern outlook, are:

Brown, G. C. (and associates). *Unit Operations.* New York, Wiley, 1950.

Dodge, B. F. *Chemical Engineering Thermodynamics.* New York, McGraw-Hill, 1944.

Hougen, O. A., and Watson, K. M. *Chemical Process Principles* (3 vols.). New York, Wiley, 1943–7.

For an account of the scientific ideas underlying chemical engineering, see:

Bosworth, R. C. L. *Physics in the Chemical Industry.* London, Macmillan, 1950.

An excellent account of current ideas and trends in chemical engineering is given in:

Gilliland, E. R. 'Problems in Chemical Engineering Research'. *Chemical Engineering Progress,* **47,** 1 (January 1951).

The engineering viewpoint is adequately explained in the following two references (both reprints of addresses):

Southwell, R. V. 'Changing Outlook of Engineering Science'. *Report of the Annual Meeting British Association 1938,* 163 (1938).

Inglis, C. E. 'Presidential Address'. *Journal of the Institution of Civil Engineers,* **17,** 1 (1941).

FUNDAMENTAL PARTICLES:
THE PRESENT SITUATION

P. E. HODGSON

READERS of *Science News* have been given the earlier chapters of the still unfolding story of the 'fundamental particles' of physics. Terence Price wrote in *Science News 16* that 'one of the characteristics of present-day nuclear physics is that the world no longer seems explicable, as it did to our grandfathers, in terms of a few fundamental units; if we are to make sense of it we have to believe in the existence of a much larger number of constituents of matter than had once been hoped'. Within two issues it was necessary to add a supplement to his article in 'Research Report', and by *Science News 21,* Professor Bhabha was suggesting that 'the circumstance that there are a dozen different types of elementary particles in nature would lead us to expect that they may be many more'. Most of these discoveries, as well as others still more recent, have been made in the first instance as a result of studies of the cosmic radiation, although in a few cases they have been confirmed and extended by the use of particles accelerated to high energies in the laboratory.

Part of the history of the subject was recounted by Professor Bhabha in his article. He recalled that it might have been thought about 1930 that 'when one knew the mathematical laws governing the behaviour of . . . protons, electrons, photons, and gravitation, one would know everything of a fundamental nature that there was to know of the physical world, and physics in principle would be a subject which had reached its destination'. But, as has happened before in physics, just as scientists thought that their knowledge was nearing completion, a flood of new discoveries came to upset their simple schemes. One of these was the discovery of the neutron by Chadwick in 1932. This enabled some difficulties connected with the structure of the atomic nucleus to be solved by assuming that it is composed of protons and neutrons in place of the old idea that it is composed of protons and electrons. But, at the same time, as Professor Bhabha pointed out, this introduced 'the possibility that, while the elementary particles are not composite and that as long as they exist they are immutable with absolutely constant properties, nevertheless there are occasions when one or more such particles can disappear altogether with the simultaneous creation of another set'. A neutron in the free state changes into a proton, an electron, and a neutrino, the last-named being an unobservable particle introduced so that the conservation laws are satisfied in the transformation. The probability of this happening is such that the rate of transformation follows the well-known exponential law, characteristic of all radioactive processes, with a half-life of about 14 minutes. This feature of instability is found even more markedly in the newly discovered fundamental particles. Some of them exist for a mere 10^{-14} seconds before undergoing a transformation.

The discovery of the neutron introduced a second new feature, the possibility that charged and neutral particles may exist which differ but little in mass. This feature also has been repeated, although on the basis of the present evidence it does not appear to be general. This may well be because the neutral particles, being more difficult to detect than their charged counterparts, have not yet been found.

Another discovery of fundamental importance was made by C. D. Anderson who, in 1931, reported the observation in a cloud chamber of the track of a particle having all the characteristics of an electron, but positively charged. It was therefore called the positron. This brought to light the occurrence of particles similar in all respects but of opposite electrical charge, and this feature has been found also in subsequent discoveries.

In 1936 Anderson and S. H. Neddermeyer observed a track in their cloud chamber which could not be ascribed to any particle known at that time. It appeared to be caused by a particle having a mass intermediate between that of the electron and that of the proton, and was accordingly called a meson. It was soon identified with a particle of similar properties that had been envisaged by the theoretician H. Yukawa in an attempt to account for the short-range nature of nuclear forces.

Work on fundamental particles was interrupted during the war years, but after the war a large number of researches soon provided a wealth of new data. As Mr. Price mentioned in his article, an experiment of Conversi, Pancini, and Piccioni in Rome showed in 1946 that the meson discovered by Anderson was not the same as that postulated by Yukawa, as it had an insufficiently strong interaction with nuclei. This difficulty was soon resolved by the discovery by Lattes, Occhialini, and Powell, at Bristol, of the transformation or decay of one type of meson, called the π-meson, into a lighter type of meson, called the μ-meson. Yukawa's meson could then be identified with the π-meson, and Anderson's with the μ-meson.

In the years that followed many observations were made which suggested the existence of heavy mesons having a mass about a thousand times that of the electron. These observations were seldom consistent with each other, and it soon became clear that more than one type of heavy meson existed. In spite of the immense amount of work that has been done, it is still a matter of extreme difficulty to obtain a coherent picture of the wealth of new phenomena that has been uncovered.

In these circumstances it is most desirable that those engaged in research should meet from time to time and discuss and attempt to correlate their findings. Such an opportunity was provided by the International Congress on the Cosmic Radiation held last July at Bagnères-de-Bigorre in the south of France. This congress, organized by the University of Toulouse under the patronage of the International Union of Pure and Applied Physics with the assistance of UNESCO, was attended by over a hundred and eighty physicists, including representatives of all the leading laboratories in the field. As a result, the discussions which took place were of a very high standard and enable authoritative conclusions on the present state of our knowledge to be drawn. The scope of the congress was mainly restricted to the field of heavy mesons, and so more detailed discussions took place than would have been possible if other aspects of the cosmic radiation had been included as well.*

The purpose of this article is to summarize the present state of our knowledge of fundamental particles as it emerged from the discussions of the congress. It is clearly impossible to refer here to each of the seventy individual papers that were presented, or the critical discussions which followed. This summary is preceded by a short discussion of the difficulties of the method of research, so that the results which follow can be appreciated in their proper perspective.

THE METHOD OF RESEARCH

Since many of the results described here are of a tentative nature, it is perhaps useful to indicate briefly the philosophy underlying this branch of research. The situation at present is that the discovery of the nature and properties of the fundamental particles is almost entirely a matter of pure experimental research. There are no comprehensive theories which could aid the experimentalist in his investigations. Practically the only theoretical laws which can be used with a high degree of confidence are such fundamental ones as the conservation of mass-energy, charge and spin.

It is accordingly up to the experimentalist to exercise his ingenuity and make as many measurements as possible on the high energy phenomena in which the fundamental particles are often found. His results may suggest that a new unstable particle be postulated which decays according to a certain scheme. In formulating this scheme he is guided by his physical intuition, by a few fundamental theoretical considerations, and by the requirement that no more complexity must be introduced than is necessary to cover the facts. He will then adopt this scheme as a tentative hypothesis and see if his data, and those of other investigators, can be consistently interpreted by it. It often hap-

*See, for example, the article by Dr E. P. George in *Science News* 27.

pens that further work brings to light new evidence which is inconsistent with the hypothesis he has made. Then he has no alternative but to modify it so as to bring it into accord with the new facts as well as the old. In this way our knowledge of fundamental particles is built up. It follows that our theories at any given time are provisional, and we may at any time be forced to revise them – as, indeed, is the case with scientific theories in general.

The situation is made more difficult by the fact that experimental results are rarely certain and can be relied upon only with a variable degree of confidence. This is particularly so in the experimental field under discussion, where the measurements are often exceedingly difficult and are subject to a host of disturbing influences which cannot easily be evaluated. Furthermore, it is nearly always possible to interpret a result indicating a new type of phenomena by means of exceedingly improbable interactions of particles that are already known. As a result it is necessary to collect a large number of results before any certain conclusions can be drawn. This makes it desirable that many groups of investigators should study similar phenomena with similar apparatus and that they should meet frequently to discuss their findings. Such an opportunity for discussion was admirably provided by the Congress of Bagnères-de-Bigorre.

The situation is made even more complicated by the lack of one-to-one correspondence between the events which are observed in the various types of experimental apparatus and the fundamental particles by which they can be interpreted. It often happens on the one hand that two very similar events are produced by two different particles while on the other hand a particular type of fundamental particle can produce dissimilar events. For these reasons it is sometimes convenient to use temporarily a 'phenomenological' classification – one in terms of appearances – so that these difficulties, if not removed, are at least minimized. Great care and skill are thus necessary in interpreting the results of experiments in this field, and it must be emphasized again that the results outlined below are in many respects provisional, and subject to revision in the light of future experience.

As some of the cosmic ray particles have an extremely high energy, much higher than can be produced by the most powerful cyclotrons or synchrotrons that exist at present or are likely to be built in the near future, the cosmic radiation is indispensable for high-energy nuclear physics. But since the cosmic radiation consists of a mixture of different types of particles going in different directions with a wide range of energies, it is difficult, in general, to make any precise and detailed investigations of any individual phenomenon occurring in it. In addition, the intensity of the cosmic radiation, especially that of the very energetic particles, is extremely small, and prolonged experiments are necessary to obtain a significant number of any particular type of event. Consequently, as soon as the particle accelerators can produce an intense, well-defined and nearly monoenergetic beam of any type of particle, it becomes much more economical to use them rather than the cosmic radiation to study the phenomena that can be produced by that particle. Thus with every advance in accelerator performance, a field of study is effectively removed from cosmic rays and given to nuclear physics.

The cosmic radiation is therefore usually responsible for discovering a new type of fundamental particle and for obtaining a qualitative survey of its properties. Then, as soon as it can be produced by accelerators, these are used to study its properties in a detailed and quantitative manner.

An excellent example of this is the π-meson, which was discovered by Professor Powell and his colleagues by exposing photographic emulsions to the cosmic radiation. They obtained an approximate value of its mass, and established its decay scheme. Now, however, the π-meson can be produced in large numbers by particle accelerators, and it is almost exclusively studied in this way. Detailed investigation of its mode of production and its nuclear interactions are being made in many laboratories in Europe and in the United States.

The cosmic-ray physicists can be thought of as explorers who first penetrate into an unknown land and make rough maps of the more prominent landmarks. Behind them come those who use particle accelerators to make an Ordnance Survey map of the new territory. It was the explorers who met at Bagnères-de-Bigorre, and it is their rough maps that are presented here.

IMPROVEMENTS IN TECHNIQUE

Before summarizing the present state of our knowledge of fundamental particles, it is convenient to describe two recent improvements in experimental technique which enable more accurate measurements to be made. The first of these is the use of stacks of stripped photographic emulsion by the Bristol group led by Professor C. F. Powell and the Bombay group led by Professor B. Peters.

The early researches using the photographic emulsion technique were made with plates consisting of a thin layer of emulsion coated on glass. The typical thickness of emulsion was about a hundred microns, and so a considerable proportion of the particles associated with any nuclear event left it before coming to rest. This is a severe limitation on the method, as grain-density and scattering measurements on short tracks do not give accurate results. Attempts were made to overcome this disadvantage by using thicker emulsions, but the thicker the emulsion the more difficult it is to process it so that the grain density of a track does not vary with depth in the emulsion. Uniformity of development is essential if accurate measurements are to be made, and in practice it is not possible to use emulsions much more than a thousand microns thick.

The new technique enables these difficulties to be overcome, and allows exposures to be made with emulsions of any desired thickness. To achieve this, the photographic emulsion is initially poured on to glass in the usual way but, after it has dried, it is stripped off the glass and assembled in stacks. A typical stack, as described by Professor Peters, contains twenty-four 6 in. × 4 in. sheets of stripped emulsion, each 600 microns thick. This stack is exposed in the normal way to the radiation under investigation. Professor Peters sent his stack to a height of about 80,000 feet by attaching it to a balloon.* After exposure, the

*See, for example, the article by A. J. Herz and R. M. Tennent in *Science News 27.*

stack is dismantled and each sheet of emulsion is stuck on to glass and processed in the usual way. If now an interesting event is found in one of the emulsions, the particles associated with it can be followed through the emulsion for a great distance from plate to plate. In this way Professor Peters has made many interesting observations which were not possible previously. There is no doubt that this technique will lead to results of the greatest importance in the future.

The second improvement in technique has been made by several groups using cloud chambers in the United States and in France. Previous work with cloud chambers has suffered from the disadvantage that of the two measurements that have to be made on the track of a particle to establish its nature and its energy only one of these, that of the curvature, could be made accurately, while the other, that of its ionization, could not, in general, be made accurately. The new technical development overcomes this by placing two cloud chambers one immediately above the other. A magnetic field applied to the top chamber enables the momentum of the particles to be found from the curvature of their tracks in the magnetic field. The lower cloud chamber contains a large number of thin lead plates. If the particle comes to rest in one of these plates after passing through the upper chamber, its residual range can be found with an uncertainty corresponding to the thickness of the plates. By combining the measurements of momentum and residual range, the nature and energy of the particle when it passed through this upper chamber can be found to a higher accuracy than was possible previously. This technique is particularly valuable for investigating particles which decay in the upper chamber giving secondaries many of which come to rest in the lead plates of the lower chamber.

NEW NOMENCLATURE

The use of the words 'fundamental particles' calls in the first place for some discussion. Clearly, as the number of 'fundamental' particles increases, it becomes less and less justifiable to use the term. The complexity of our present knowledge of them suggests that the particles we call 'fundamental' are in fact some kinds of structures composed of even more subtle entities. Nevertheless the word 'fundamental' is retained for the present.

A similar objection could be made to the use here of the word 'particle', with all its Newtonian billiard-ball associations. In fact, as we know, 'fundamental particles' are entities which we cannot imagine, but which behave in some circumstances like the particles and in others like the waves we encounter in our everyday experience. In reality they are neither particles nor waves, but entities to which our crude concepts apply solely in an analogous way. We have for so long been accustomed to call them 'fundamental particles' that this usage is continued here. But its defects must not be forgotten, and it must not be taken as implying any finality in our present knowledge.

In order to provide a more systematic classification of the bewildering variety of 'fundamental' particles, several improvements in nomenclature were decided upon at Bagnères-de-Bigorre. Although these cannot be considered 'official', as they have yet to be internationally accepted, they have nevertheless considerable authority behind them on account of the large number of leading specialists who attended the Bagnères congress.

The nomenclature can be conveniently considered in three sections: Firstly, all particles are divided into groups according to the range in which their mass lies. Secondly, different types of events are classified phenomologically. Thirdly, each different particle is given its symbol.

(1) *Groups of Particles*

L-mesons. Particles with mass greater than that of the electron and up to, and including, that of the π-meson.

K-mesons. Particles with mass intermediate between that of the π-meson and that of the neutron. These are often referred to as 'heavy mesons'.

Hyperons. Particles with mass intermediate between that of the proton and that of the deuteron. (This defini-

> tion may have to be revised if 'fundamental' par-
> ticles heavier than the deuteron are found.)

Small Greek letters are used for mesons and capital Greek letters for hyperons.

(2) *Phenomenological Description*

V-event. Phenomena which can be interpreted as the decay in flight of a *K*-meson or hyperon. These events were first observed in a cloud chamber and consist of two tracks in the form of a 'V'. *V*-events are subclassified as $V°$ and $V\pm$ according as the decaying particle is neutral or charged.

S-event. Phenomena which can be interpreted as the decay or nuclear capture of a *K*-meson or hyperon that has stopped in the cloud chamber or photographic emulsion.

(3) *Names of individual types of particles*

These are considered in the next section.

THE PRESENT STATE OF KNOWLEDGE

A list is given below of the fundamental particles that are known at present, together with their properties. The more well known among these are included for completeness, although they were not discussed at Bagnères. All masses are expressed as multiples of the electronic mass. The limits of error that are given are intended as indications of the degree of accuracy obtainable at present rather than as precise standard deviations, which in many cases cannot be given as the results have been obtained by combining the observations of different groups of investigators using different apparatus of more or less precision. The kinetic energies released in the decay of the fundamental particles are known as *Q*-values; they are usually calculated on the assumption of a particular decay-scheme, which is often partly hypothetical. If future work necessitates the modification of these decay schemes, the corresponding *Q*-values will have to be re-calculated. These *Q*-values are in million electron-volts (MeV).

Gamma ray (γ). Electromagnetic radiation. The frequency of a γ-ray can have any value and, the higher the frequency, the more energetic is the γ-ray. If its energy is high enough, a γ-ray can interact with a nucleus to give a nuclear disintegration or a pair of electrons.

Neutrino (ν). An uncharged particle postulated to conserve momentum, energy and spin in nuclear transformations (see earlier in this article). Mass, very small or zero.

Electron ($e^{\pm}$). e^+ is also called the positron. Stable, but an e^+ and an e^- interact to give a pair of γ-rays. Mass, 1.

L-MESONS

$\mu^{\pm}$-*meson*. Mass, 210 ± 2. Lifetime, 2.2×10^{-6} seconds. Positive or negative.

Decay scheme: $\mu^{\pm} \longrightarrow e^{\pm} + 2\nu$ (Q, about 105 MeV)

The emitted electron has a variable energy up to a maximum of 55 MeV, with a mean of about 36 MeV. This variation in energy shows that at least two other particles must be emitted for energy and momentum to be conserved. The negative μ-meson has a weak interaction with nuclei and can produce a low-energy nuclear disintegration (one with an excitation energy of not more than about 15 MeV), if it does not decay first. μ-mesons are produced by decay of the π-meson or by that of the κ-meson (see later).

π°-*meson*. Mass, 266 ± 3. Lifetime, about 10^{-14} seconds. Neutral.

Decay scheme: $\pi^{\circ} \longrightarrow 2\gamma$ (Q, about 133 MeV)

or $\pi^{\circ} \longrightarrow \gamma + e^+ + e^-$ (very rarely)

Neutral π-mesons are produced in high-energy collisions between nucleons (protons or neutrons).

$\pi^{\pm}$-*meson*. Mass, 276 ± 2. Lifetime, 2.6×10^{-8} seconds. Positive or negative.

Decay scheme: $\pi^{\pm} \longrightarrow \mu^{\pm} + \nu$ (Q, about 33 MeV; energy of μ-meson, about 4 MeV)

If nuclei are present, the negative π-meson can be captured, giving a nuclear disintegration of excitation energy about 100 MeV. Charged π-mesons are produced in collisions between nucleons along with the neutral π-mesons.

K-MESONS

ζ°-*meson*. Mass, about 550. Lifetime, less than 10^{-14} seconds. Neutral.

Decay scheme: $\zeta^\circ \longrightarrow \pi^+ + \pi^-$　　(Q, about 2 MeV)

The existence of this particle is suggested by the observation of correlated pairs of π-mesons emitted from high-energy nuclear interactions. Since it is almost certain that this can be accounted for by a strong mutual interaction between π-mesons, the evidence for the ζ°-meson is very weak.

$\zeta\pm$-*meson*. Mass, about 530. Lifetime, greater than 10^{-11} seconds. Positive or negative. Decay scheme, unknown.

The existence of this particle is suggested by some measurements on the multiple scattering of a few tracks in photographic emulsions. Owing to the difficulties of such measurements, the evidence for this particle is extremely weak.

τ°-*meson*. Mass, about 1000. Lifetime, ?

Decay scheme: $\tau^\circ \longrightarrow \pi^+ + \pi^- + \pi^\circ$　　(Q, less than 75 MeV)

There are two or three cloud-chamber photographs which suggest this decay scheme, but the evidence at present is very weak.

$\tau\pm$-*meson*. Mass, 970 ± 2. Lifetime, 10^{-8} to 10^{-10} seconds. Probably positive and negative.

Decay scheme: $\tau\pm \longrightarrow \pi\pm + \pi^+ + \pi^-$　　($Q = 76\pm2$ MeV)

These properties of the τ-meson are well established by photographic plate and by cloud-chamber measurements.

θ°-*meson*. Mass 971 ± 10. Lifetime, about 10^{-10} seconds. Neutral.

Decay scheme: $\theta^\circ \longrightarrow \pi^+ + \pi^-$　　($Q = 214\pm5$ MeV)

The θ°-meson has so far been indicated only by cloud-chamber measurements. It was first described as the V_2° particle, and later as the $V_4°$ particle, when it was realized that more than one kind of particle had been included in the first of these descriptions. The possibility of the decay scheme, $\theta° \longrightarrow \pi^+ + \pi^- + n$, where n represents a neutron, cannot be completely ruled out. If the $\theta°$-meson decays in this way, its mass is greater than that of the proton, and so it should then be classed as a hyperon.

$\kappa^{\pm}$-*meson.* Mass, 990 ± 30. Lifetime, about 10^{-9} seconds. Probably positive and negative.

Decay scheme: $\kappa^{\pm} \longrightarrow \mu^{\pm} + 2\nu$ (Q, about 400 MeV)

The emitted μ-meson has a variable energy up to a maximum of about 180 MeV. There is some evidence in favour of one of the secondaries being a γ-ray. This particle was first indicated by measurements made in photographic plates. It is likely that most of the charged V-particles that are observed in cloud chambers are κ-mesons.

$\chi^{\pm}$-*meson.* Mass, about 1000. Lifetime, ?. Probably positive and negative.

Decay scheme: $\chi^{\pm} \longrightarrow \pi^{\pm} + \nu$ (Q, about 720 MeV; energy of π-meson, 116 ± 10 MeV)

It is assumed that the χ-meson decays into two particles because measurements on the secondaries found so far are consistent with a constant energy of emission of the π-meson. The evidence for the secondary particles being π-mesons is strong but not conclusive. There is no evidence as to the nature of the neutral secondary; it may well be a γ-ray or a $\pi°$-meson. The existence of the χ-meson has been established by measurements in photographic emulsion, but it is likely that some of the charged V-particles observed in cloud chambers are also χ-mesons.

η-*meson.* Mass, ? (depends on the exact decay scheme; see below, where the two secondaries are allocated only to the K and L groups of particles). Neutral.

Decay scheme: $\eta \longrightarrow K + L$ (Q, very approximately, 60 MeV)

This particle is indicated by some cloud-chamber observations made by R. B. Leighton of the California Institute of Technology group. It has sometimes been called the $V_3°$ particle. The identification of the secondaries of this decay is extremely weak.

NUCLEONS

Proton (p). Mass, 1836. Stable. Positively charged.

Neutron (n). Mass, 1838. Lifetime, about 14 minutes. Neutral.

HYPERONS

$\Omega°$-*particle*. Mass, 2184 ± 7. Lifetime, $(3.3 \pm 1) \times 10^{-10}$ seconds. Neutral.

Decay scheme: $\Omega° \longrightarrow p^+ + \pi^-$ (Q, 37 ± 3 MeV)

The existence of this particle was first indicated by the observation of $V_1°$ tracks in cloud chambers. Considerable evidence for their observation in photographic plates as well was presented at the Congress.

Up to the time of the Congress, it had been an open question whether the $\Omega°$ particle was an 'excited state' of a nucleon produced by exciting a pre-existing nucleon or whether it was a 'fundamental' particle which could be produced completely from the kinetic energy of colliding nucleons. At the Congress, however, Dr N. Kaplon reported that a $V°$-particle of kinetic energy 714 ± 150 MeV had been produced by protons of 2,300 MeV from the Brookhaven synchrotron. This suggests that the former of the two alternatives takes place, as there is insufficient energy available for the second. It is, of course, possible that the second process takes place at higher energies, but at present there is no evidence for the production of nucleons in high-energy collisions.

$\Omega^\pm$-*particle*. Mass ?

Decay schemes: $\Omega^+ \longrightarrow p^+ + (?\pi°)$
$$\Omega^\pm \longrightarrow n° + (?\pi^\pm)$$ (Q, about 130 MeV)

Neither of these decay schemes is established beyond doubt, but the evidence for the second is rather better than that for the first.

V^{*-}-*particle*. Mass ?

Decay scheme: $V^{*-} \longrightarrow \Omega + L^-$

The existence of this particle was first indicated when the Manchester group observed two V-decays in a cloud chamber, one above the other. The lower, a $V°$-decay, was almost in line with the primary of the upper, which was a $V^{\pm}$-decay. Since, however, such an isolated event could be due to the chance coincidence of two V-decays not related by the above scheme, no definite conclusions could be drawn from it. At the Bagnères congress, however, Dr Leighton reported the observation of three more examples of these 'cascade decays', as they are called. This greatly increases the likelihood that the V^{*-}-particle exists, although, of course, it is by no means established.

In addition to the phenomena which can be interpreted by the particles listed above, there are other phenomena whose existence is quite well established, but whose interpretation is uncertain.

Among these is the disintegration of a nucleus by a heavy meson. Four examples were reported by Professor Peters at the congress, and two or three others have been published in the past few years. The nature of the primary particle cannot be established, but it seems plausible to attribute most of these events to negative τ-mesons. This interpretation will be strengthened if it is found, by experiments like that of Professor Peters, that all the τ-mesons decaying into three π-mesons are positive. The τ-meson will then be analogous to the π-meson, in that when negative it interacts with a nucleus causing it to disintegrate and when positive it decays into three particles. Negative κ- and χ-mesons may also cause some of these events.

Another type of phenomena in which the existence of heavy mesons is established is in the very high energy nuclear interactions known as 'jets', which have been extensively studied by the Bristol group under Professor Powell and by others. When two nucleons collide at extremely high energies (upwards of a million MeV) a number of mesons, which may be as high as ten or twenty, is produced. These are emitted in a very narrow stream or jet.* These mesons are mostly π-mesons, but the Bristol

*An example was reproduced as Inset 29 in *Science News 27.*

group has shown by measurements of the multiple scattering and ionization of these particles in photographic emulsion that some of them are heavy mesons. The proportion of heavy mesons in these jets increases with the energy of the collision. It has not yet, however, been established which types of heavy mesons are present in jets. It seems likely, of course, that all types of heavy mesons are present in proportions that vary with energy. An alternative possibility is that some of the types of heavy mesons are produced only by the decay of still heavier particles which are themselves produced in nucleon-nucleon collisions.

DISCUSSION OF THESE RESULTS

The brief summary given above of the properties of the fundamental particles that are at present known to us gives little idea either of the complexity of the problems which arise in establishing them or of the wealth and variety of the experimental data. Many long and critical discussions on the various possibilities took place at the congress. It is not possible to do more than briefly indicate a few of them here.

It was pointed out that the two heavy mesons whose existence is most securely established, namely the τ- and the $\theta°$-mesons, have masses which only differ by less than about 10 electron masses. This suggests that perhaps the masses are identical, and that the τ- and $\theta°$-mesons represent alternative modes of decay of the same fundamental particle. This was discussed at the congress, but no firm conclusion was reached.

Another possibility is that the τ-, χ-, and κ-mesons are similarly different modes of decay of the same fundamental particle. Considerable discussion took place on the problem of whether the mass of the χ-meson could be identical with that of the τ-meson. The situation at present is that all measurements on particles coming to rest and decaying give an average mass of 990 ± 30, which is consistent with that of the τ-meson. Unfortunately, however, the accurate measurements of Perkins and his colleagues on the heavy mesons in jets, which probably include a considerable proportion of χ-mesons, indicate a mass of about 1200. It is most unlikely that this value is consistent

1. Distillation: fractionating towers on the distillation unit, Shell chemical plant, Stanlow (*by courtesy of the Shell Petroleum Company, Ltd*). The evolution from laboratory-type equipment to continuous, large-scale operation is shown in the three following pictures.

2. Distillation: use of laboratory-type equipment (two distillation units at back) in chemical preparations for bleachers and Turkey Red dyers, 1820. (*From* The Chemical Revolution *by Archibald and Nan Clow, Batchworth Press, by courtesy of the authors and publishers.*)

3. Distillation: a bench of stills used early in the present century for the distillation of petroleum. Each still held some thousands of gallons. The earliest continuously operating plant was evolved from stills of this type.

4. Distillation: continuous operation. Fractionating tower of single-stage unit for the fractional distillation of crude petroleum at the Esso refinery, Fawley. (*By courtesy of the Esso Petroleum Company, Ltd.*)

5. Night view of the Esso refinery, Fawley. The catalytic cracking unit (Inset 7), by which the yield of the lighter fractions is increased, is near the left of the picture. (*By courtesy of the Esso Petroleum Company, Ltd.*)

6. General view of the Shell chemical plant, Stanlow, taken at dusk. The tower of the cracking unit is on the left; on the right, fractionating towers. (*By courtesy of the Shell Petroleum Company, Ltd.*)

7. Catalytic cracking unit, Esso refinery, Fawley. (*By courtesy of the Esso Petroleum Company, Ltd.*)

8. Hydrogenation of coal: replica, erected at the Fuel Research Station, Greenwich, in the late 1920s, of the original pilot-plant (at Mannheim) for the Bergius process. (*Fuel Research Station, Crown copyright.*)

9. Hydrogenation of coal: general arrangement of hydrogenation stalls at the Billingham petrol plant. (*By courtesy of Imperial Chemical Industries, Ltd.*)

10. To show limb-darkening towards the edge of the sun's disc: the effect must be allowed for in stellar interferometry. (*Royal Observatory, Greenwich.*)

11. Spaced-aerial radio interferometer constructed at Cambridge for the accurate location of radio stars; the aerial separation is about 1,350 ft. (*M. Ryle, F.R.S., Cavendish Laboratory, Cambridge.*)

12. Because of the small space which they need for landing and take-off, helicopters are being intensively used in geophysical prospecting for oil in Netherlands New Guinea. A helicopter and its hangar are shown arrowed at a riverside base-camp.

13. Unloading by Papuans at a jungle landing-ground. (*Photographs by courtesy of the Shell Petroleum Company.*)

14. The facility of the helicopter for close flying in difficult mountain country crossed in many places by overhead cables led to its use by Pest Control in a plant-spraying operation in the Canton Valais, Rhone Valley.

15. Showing the clearly defined 'swarth' delivered by the helicopter. (*Photographs by courtesy of Pest Control, Ltd.*)

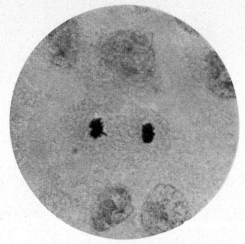

16. A normal cell in division. The chromosomes are seen as two separate clumps.

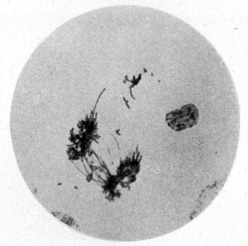

17. A cell from a tumour in the rat after treatment with a nitrogen mustard. Chromosome bridges and fragments are shown.

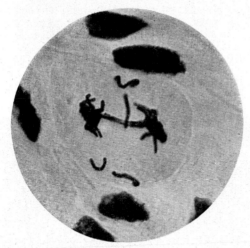

18. A cell from a bean-root grown in a solution of radiomimetic agent. As in Inset 17, chromosome bridges and fragments are shown.

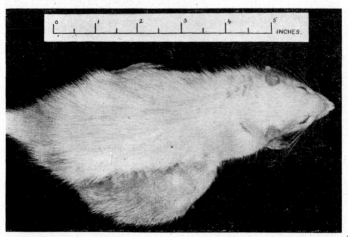

19. A rat bearing an experimental Walker tumour as used to measure the effect of radiomimetic chemicals in inhibiting tumour-growth.

PLATINUM METALS EXHIBITION

The 150th anniversary of the announcement, through an anonymously issued handbill, of the discovery of the new metal, palladium, by William Hyde Wollaston, later President of the Royal Society, was the occasion of an exhibition arranged by the Institution of Metallurgists to illustrate the history and uses of the platinum metals. The photographs on this and the following four pages are reproduced, by permission of the Institution, from the handbook of the exhibition.

20. The obverse of the Wollaston Medal of the Geological Society; it is awarded annually for outstanding researches concerning the mineral structure of the earth.

PALLADIUM;

OR,

NEW SILVER,

HAs these Properties, amongst others that shew it to be

A NEW NOBLE METAL.

1. IT dissolves in pure Spirit of Nitre, and makes a dark red solution.

2. Green Vitriol throws it down in the state of a regulus from this solution, as it always does Gold from *Aqua Regia*.

3. IF you evaporate the solution you get a red calx that dissolves in Spirit of Salt or other acids.

4. IT is thrown down by quicksilver and by all the metals but Gold, Platina, and Silver.

5. ITS Specific Gravity by hammering was only 11.3, but by flatting as much as 11.8.

6. IN a common fire the face of it tarnishes a little and turns blue, but comes bright again, like other noble metals on being stronger heated.

7. THE greatest heat of a blacksmith's fire would hardly melt it;

8. BUT if you touch it while hot with a small bit of Sulphur it runs as easily as Zinc.

IT IS SOLD ONLY BY

MR. FORSTER, at No. 26, GERRARD STREET, SOHO,
LONDON.

In Samples of Five Shillings, Half a Guinea, & One Guinea each.

J. Moore, Printer, Drury Lane

21. One of the handbills distributed anonymously by Wollaston in 1803 to announce his discovery of palladium. (*Department of Mineralogy and Petrology, the University of Cambridge.*)

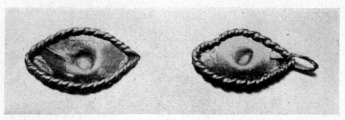

22. Ornaments of native platinum and gold, about half an inch long, made by South American Indians before the discovery of America by Europeans. (*Museum of the American Indian, Heye Foundation, New York.*)

23. Assembly of counterfeit 'gold' coins, in fact of gilded platinum, which were put into circulation in various European countries around the middle of the 19th century. (*Royal Belgian Mint.*)

24. Rolling pure platinum strip.

25. A platinum-rhodium gauze for a 3-metre diameter ammonia burner.

26. A platinum-rhodium thermocouple being used to determine the temperature of liquid steel.

with a mass of 990. It is conceivable that particles of mass about 1200 are produced in jets, and that these decay in flight into particles of mass about 990 which in turn come to rest before they decay. There is, however, no evidence to support this hypothesis. The solution of this problem must await further accurate experimental determinations of the masses of these particles, but it was generally considered that the identification of the masses of the χ- and τ-mesons was quite plausible, while the further identification of this mass with that of the χ-meson was considerably less likely.

A number of subsidiary considerations, of varying weight, which bear on these problems can be derived from the frequencies with which these particles are observed to decay in flight and at rest in photographic emulsions and in cloud chambers. But as the data at present available refer to particles of a wide range of energies and to apparatus exposed to the cosmic radiation at different heights above sea level and, in the case of the cloud chambers, triggered by different arrangements of counters, it is difficult to draw any firm conclusions from it.

These discussions on the possible identity of some of the types of heavy mesons underlined the need for more experiments of a high degree of accuracy. As long as the experiments give results with rather wide limits of error the discussions will continue to be inconclusive. This was emphasized by Professor P. M. S. Blackett, the President of the Congress, in his address. The new types of apparatus which were described by several speakers give great promise that new measurements of a high degree of accuracy will be made in the near future, and we can therefore confidently look forward to an early solution of these problems.

THE OUTLOOK FOR THE FUTURE

In his concluding address to the Congress, Professor L. Leprince Ringuet, its Scientific Secretary, illustrated with characteristic felicity and humour the present position of workers in the field of cosmic radiation. Referring to the fact that more and more of their work is being taken over by physicists using accelerators, he thought of them as mountaineers climbing the precipitous slopes of the energy spectrum. As they struggle upwards towards peaks still shrouded in mist, every step is more painful than the last as the experimental difficulties multiply. Furthermore, an angry sea surrounding the mountain continually rises as their territory is reduced by accelerators producing particles of still higher energy. The plight of the cosmic-ray physicists is indeed a desperate one, with the howling gales of experimental errors lashing them from above and the biting waves of the accelerators eating away their foothold from below.

In spite of these difficult circumstances, however, there is still a vast field of investigation open to the cosmic-ray physicists. Nuclear interactions of the very highest energy can only be studied by using the particles found in the cosmic radiation. Professor Schein, for example, has reported a collision of a proton of about thirty million MeV with another proton in a photographic emulsion in which some fifteen mesons were produced. It will be a very long time before such energies can be attained by atom-smashing machines.

But while the cosmic-ray physicists will always have a field of study beyond the reach of the accelerators, much of their present domain will soon be taken over by a number of large machines that have just been completed or are under construction. The proton synchrotron, or 'Cosmotron', at Brookhaven in the United States has already produced protons of 2,300 MeV, and these are being used to study the production of V-particles and other high-energy phenomena. A similar machine is almost complete at Berkeley, California, and this should accelerate protons to about 6,400 MeV, and the Birmingham protron synchrotron has recently come into operation. Several accelerators will be built at the European Nuclear Physics Centre at Geneva. These include a synchrocyclotron to accelerate protons to 600 MeV and a proton synchrotron for energies from 10,000 to 30,000 MeV. The cost of these machines is very high, and it becomes prohibitively so for proton energies above about 30,000 MeV. Recently, however, members of the Brookhaven laboratory have suggested a new method of focusing the particles which should permit accelerating tubes of much smaller diameter to be used, thus greatly reducing their cost. The new focusing system has many complex problems of its own, but if they are successfully solved, it may permit energies as high as 100,000 MeV to be attained.*

These machines will allow many types of mesons and hyperons to be produced in large numbers under accurately controlled experimental conditions. It is likely that many new types of unstable particles will be discovered, and that it will be possible in time to determine their properties to a high degree of accuracy.

It should be emphasized that the detection of these unstable particles of very short lifetime is a matter of extreme difficulty, and that we have so far found only those particles which our apparatus can detect. There probably exist very many more particles whose detection is not possible at present. Suppose, for example, that there is a neutral μ-meson which decays into two neutrinos. Such a particle would be almost impossible to detect.

It is clear that at the present time experiments on high-energy particles, in spite of their difficulty, are opening up a field of very great complexity and interest. It is probable that the situation will become even more complex before it can be simplified into a unified scheme.

If the difficulties of the experimentalist are very great, those of the theoreticians are even greater. At present it appears a hopeless task to attempt to provide a theoretical framework for the heavy mesons when such a scheme has not yet been satisfactorily formulated even for the π- and μ-mesons, whose properties are known in considerable detail to a high degree of accuracy. It seems likely that a great many more accurate experimental results will have to be collected before some regularities become evident, which may suggest the beginnings of such a theoretical scheme.

*Plans for the construction of proton synchrotons (up to the Berkeley machine) were summarized by Dr L. L. Green in his article 'The Acceleration of Charged Particles to High Energies' in *Science News 22*; a preliminary note on the new focusing principle was given in *Science News 27*, 115–16.

It is probable that such a scheme will not be formulated for many years. It will no doubt be of a more profound nature than the rather crude extrapolations along semi-classical lines which have served up till now. It will link into a unified whole all the properties of the particles that are at present called 'fundamental' and will enable their interactions to be calculated. Such is the goal towards which the experiments and calculations of physicists are aimed, but many centuries may well pass before it is achieved.

CHEMICAL RADIOMIMETIC
AGENTS AND CANCER

R. F. HOMER

WHEN living cells are subjected to irradiation with x rays or other short-wave radiation such as the gamma-radiation from radioactive substances certain characteristic abnormalities are produced inside the cell nucleus. These abnormalities, which are probably caused during the resting stage of the life cycle of the cell, and which have come to be known as 'specific chromosome effects', only become evident during division, or mitosis, of the affected cells, when observation under the microscope reveals far-reaching disorganization of the chromosomes. When a normal cell divides, each of the several chromosomes splits along its length and the identical halves of each (called chromatids) migrate to opposite ends of the cell, there forming two new chromosome systems which are exact replicas of the parent system, and which make up the nuclei of the two new cells resulting from the subsequent division of the protoplasm. The chromosomes of irradiated cells on the other hand, in their attempt at division, either break up into several fragments which scatter at random, or else 'bridges' are formed between adjacent chromatids which prevent their separation towards the opposite ends of the cell (Inset 16–18). As a result of this damage the cell usually dies, or in a small proportion of cases where damage is less severe, division is accomplished and leads to two mutated cells with deficient or abnormal chromosome structures. These latter cells may survive and give rise to progeny carrying replicas of the original deficient chromosome system through many divisions, or may die after a few generations. The killing effect of the severe damage to chromosome structure caused by intensive x-irradiation has led to the use of x rays in conjunction with surgery, in the control of malignant cancers. It is probably the mutating effect of exposure of normal cells to a low dose of x rays over a long period which gives rise to a higher proportion of less-badly damaged viable cells, which may eventually produce, by chance, a malignant mutant. This abnormal cell divides rapidly and unchecked causing radiation cancer.

This characteristic type of cell damage was until recently known to be produced only by short wave-length high energy radiation and it was quite accidental that it was discovered during World War II that certain chemical compounds, christened radiomimetic agents from the way in which their effect on the cell mimicked that caused by radiation, could produce effects in the cell almost indistinguishable from those caused by radiation. During a search for potential vesicant war gases a class of compounds known by the general name of nitrogen mustards came to be investigated. The compounds are related chemically to the well-known 'mustard gas' of World War I (Fig. 1). In this, a central sulphur atom links two chlorethyl groups ($Cl—CH_2CH_2—$), the complete compound being described as $\beta:\beta'$-dichlorodiethylsulphide. The nitrogen mustards differ from mustard gas in having a nitrogen atom in place of the central sulphur atom, and a further group R (Fig. 2) which in the original compounds examined was either hydrogen, methyl, or a third β-chloroethyl group.

$$Cl—CH_2CH_2—S—CH_2CH_2—Cl$$

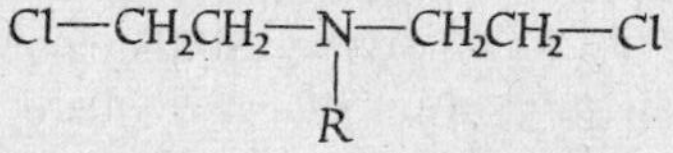

$$Cl—CH_2CH_2—N—CH_2CH_2—Cl$$
$$|$$
$$R$$

Fig. 1. 'Mustard gas.'   Fig. 2. The nitrogen mustards.

Intensive subsequent chemical work has led to the synthesis of many related compounds in which R has been varied, and all have been found to possess radiomimetic activity to a greater or less extent, according to the effect of the group R on the reactivity of the chlorine atoms. To these atoms was also attributed the vesicant action of the mustards, both nitrogen and sulphur. It had indeed been long believed that the action of sulphur mustard was due solely to hydrochloric acid, released beneath the skin by the splitting off of the chlorine atoms as ions from the mustard through reaction with the water of tissue fluids. It soon became clear, however, that the cell damage inflicted was far greater than could be accounted for by the very small amount of hydrochloric acid liberated from the quantity of mustard required to produce the damage. During a search for effective antidotes to the nitrogen mustards it was discovered that they had, in addition to a local vesicant action, a far-reaching general systemic effect at a high dose-level which was most marked on the rapidly dividing cells of the body, for example the blood-forming organs, and the intestinal mucosa. The cells of the latter ceased to divide and suffered extensive gross damage leading to destruction and necrosis of the tissue. Also at a much lower, relatively non-toxic, dose-level the mustards caused the characteristic chromosome damage described above, previously associated only with radiation.

Intensive work carried out semi-secretly during the later years of the war, in this country and in the United States, revealed that the nitrogen mustards considerably slowed down the growth of experimental cancers in animals and in some cases led to their complete eradication (Inset 19). This effect was caused by the drug preventing division of the malignant cells, thereby leading to their death. The growth-inhibiting effect was unfortunately not confined exclusively to the cancerous tissue but was general throughout the body of the animal; however it appeared that by choice of a suitable dose level generalized damage could be minimized and useful effects still obtained on the tumour. This was explained in part by the greater proportion of dividing cells relative to the rest of the body in the rapidly growing malignant tissue, with the added postulation of a more efficient 'repair mechanism' in normal cells compared with malignant cells. With the lifting of security precautions and the return to free publication after the war, a widespread examination of the effects of these compounds in malignant diseases in higher experimental animals and in humans was carried out. It was soon apparent that any hope that nitrogen mustards might be a cure for cancer was groundless, though the compounds showed a considerable palliative effect in cases of leukaemia, a malignant disorder of the blood characterized by a rapid and unchecked rise in the number of leucocytes, and also in Hodgkin's disease, a cancer of the lymphatic system, both sites where it had been previously shown that the mustards exerted their greatest toxic effects. Unfortunately the palliative effect was only temporary and though remissions of the symptoms of the disease of up to two or three years were obtained in favourable cases the condition eventually became resistant to treatment, as it similarly becomes resistant to treatment with x rays, and the patients finally succumbed. Nevertheless nitrogen mustards have become established as one of the treatments of choice for these two complaints. Though possibly more convenient than x-ray therapy the chemical reactivity of these compounds is such that a special injection technique has to be used and very close control of dosage routine maintained, necessitating hospitalization of the patient. The mustards have not so far been shown to have any effect on solid tumours in humans, where radiation is more efficacious since it can be applied in high intensity locally to the tumour, while nitrogen mustards can only be administered in such a way that they become generally distributed through the body, and so do not attain a higher concentration in the tumour than elsewhere. The encouraging results obtained in animal experiments, in which it is possible to give much higher relative doses of drugs than in humans, were therefore not reproduced in clinical usage.

The mode of action of these radiomimetic compounds was the subject of much early speculation, and it was believed that the drug reacted with some cell component containing in its molecules chemical groups with a replaceable hydrogen atom such as an amino group ($-NH_2$), hydroxyl ($-OH$) or sulphydryl ($-SH$) group, thereby blocking an essential metabolic system necessary for orderly mitosis. An example of such a reaction, involving combination of a mustard with an amino compound, is shown below:

$$-N-CH_2CH_2Cl + H_2NR' \rightarrow -N-CH_2CH_2NHR' + HCl$$

This type of reaction is described as alkylation. Its effect is to join an alkyl group, for example methyl or ethyl, or a substituted alkyl group on to the nitrogen, sulphur, or oxygen atom in place of the hydrogen atom. It will be noticed that only one of the chloroethyl groups of the mustard is included in the diagram; the other one, or possibly two, could react similarly.

With the idea of producing further types of compound which would react with active hydrogen atoms in biological molecules a whole range of chemically reactive substances was synthesized.* Eventually, after many materials had been made, which were biologically inactive, an active type was discovered in the methylolamides; these are compounds containing one or more $-NHCH_2OH$ groups which, like the chloroethyl groups of the mustards, can react, for example with $-NH_2$, giving in this case $-NHCH_2NH-$ by elimination of water, and it was found that for activity to be obtained at least three $-NHCH_2OH$ groups were necessary in the drug molecule. The methylolamides were found to be in general of very low toxicity, but massive doses were required to produce any useful biological effects. In addition they were very unstable, giving rise readily to water-insoluble partially polymerized forms which were difficult to administer and also on storage they tended to liberate the very toxic formaldehyde. The highest degree of activity encountered in this type of compound was found in trimethylol melamine (Figure 3, *overleaf*) and in several closely related substances.

The original idea of examining the methylolamides arose from a study of the apparently unrelated field of textile and paper technology in which it had been shown that these substances were capable of combining with cellulosic $-OH$ groups in cotton or paper and $-NH_2$ or $-SH$ groups in wool protein to confer certain properties such as crease resistance and anti-shrink properties in textile fabrics, and increased wet-strength in

*Such as isocyanates, halogen compounds, ketones, etc

paper. These effects were produced by a cross-linkage between adjacent cellulose or protein fibres which imparted a certain rigidity to the fibre structure. Simultaneously with these observations it had been observed by another group of workers that for radiomimetic activity to be present more than one β-chloroethyl group was necessary in the nitrogen mustards. This fact led to a

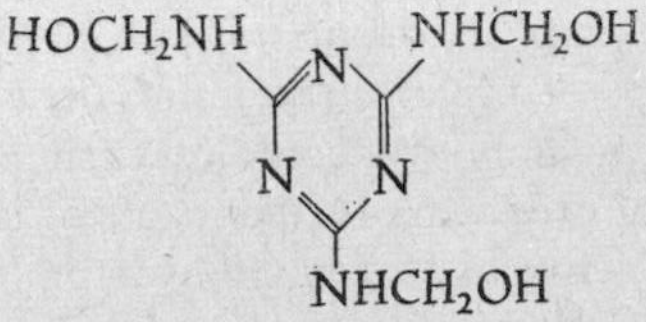

$$HOCH_2NH \qquad NHCH_2OH$$

$$NHCH_2OH$$

Fig. 3. Trimethylol melamine.

further theory that the drug acted by some 'cross-linking' mechanism involving reaction of both ends of the drug molecule with two centres in the cell constituent. It was postulated therefore that the drug linked together the adjacent nucleoprotein chains which make up the chromosome structure, thus mechanically preventing division of the chromosome during mitosis, and so explaining on a mechanical basis the observed fragmentation, 'bridging' and 'looping' of the chromosomes. This theory is now widely accepted as being at least a first approximation to the truth and experimental evidence has been obtained in its favour from the fact that treatment of isolated nucleic acid with a mustard leads to an apparent doubling of its molecular size. Chemical work has shown that the nitrogen mustard molecule can rearrange itself to form an ionic chloride, that is, a negative chlorine ion and a positive (basic) ion. The latter can react with ionized acidic groups, for example carboxylic or phosphoric, these being almost certainly the cell components attacked. The basic ion which reacts with them is marked (I) below; it has the cyclic immonium ion structure, so called in distinction from the simple ammonium ion. It is relatively unstable, and a further rearrangement, involving reaction with the carboxylate ion, leads to the final compound, an ester.

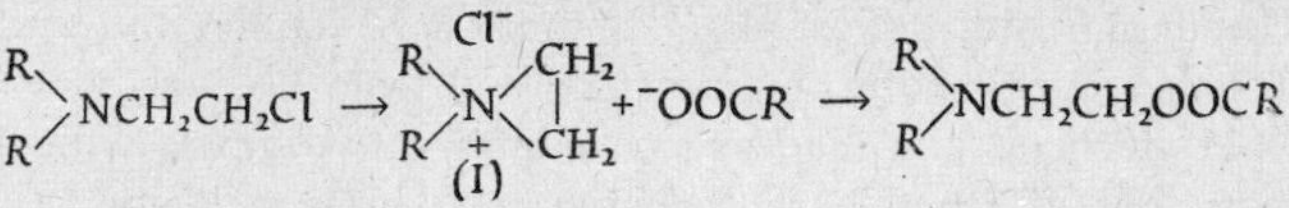

$$R_2NCH_2CH_2Cl \rightarrow R_2\overset{+}{N}\overset{Cl^-}{\underset{(I)}{\begin{array}{c}CH_2\\ \mid\\ CH_2\end{array}}} + {}^-OOCR \rightarrow R_2NCH_2CH_2OOCR$$

Thus the picture shown in Figure 4 was evolved where a number of drug molecules act as links between adjacent nucleoprotein chains. At least two reactive groups are thus assumed. A further later modification of this theory which explained certain important discoveries made concerning the activity of the methylol-amides, in which at least three reactive groups were necessary in the drug molecule before activity was obtained, will be discussed later.

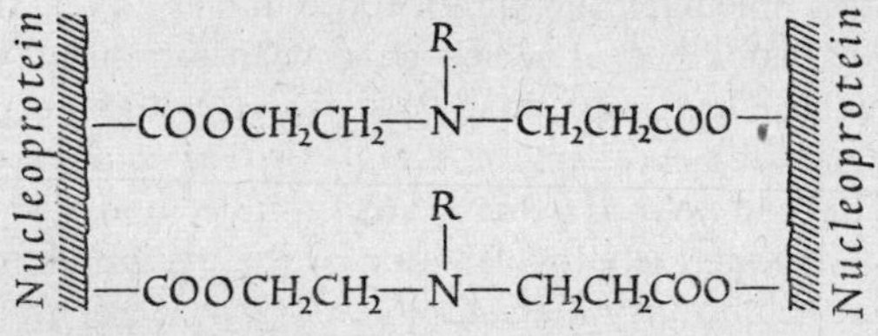

$$\text{Nucleoprotein} \left[\begin{array}{l} -COOCH_2CH_2-\overset{R}{\underset{|}{N}}-CH_2CH_2COO- \\ \\ -COOCH_2CH_2-\overset{R}{\underset{|}{N}}-CH_2CH_2COO- \end{array} \right] \text{Nucleoprotein}$$

Fig. 4. To illustrate the cross-linking theory.

Acceptance of the cross-linking theory stimulated chemists to search for other cross-linking agents which might have the same therapeutic action in an enhanced degree, or without the toxic side reactions such as nausea and vomiting associated with the nitrogen mustards, and especially for compounds sufficiently stable to be taken by mouth or injected by normal techniques. Here again help was forthcoming from the field of textile chemistry where in addition to the methylolamides there were being investigated in certain laboratories two classes of compounds of special interest:

the ethylene oxides containing two or more $-\overset{O}{\overset{/\backslash}{CH-CH_2}}$ groups

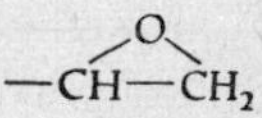

and the ethylene imines containing two or more $\overset{N}{\underset{CH_2-CH_2}{\overset{/\backslash}{}}}$ groups

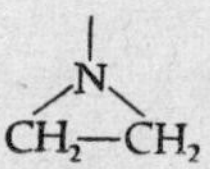

The designation 'imine', like 'immonium', denotes the cyclic structure shown in the diagram at foot of page 75. Each of these types of chemically reactive compound will combine with the same type of reactive centre, in particular an acid ion, as is attacked by the β-chloroethyl moiety, thus an ethylene oxide will react with a carboxylic acid ion to give the ester —$COOCH_2CH$ $(OH)R$. It was, in fact, found that these classes of compound possessed a high degree of radiomimetic activity and that again at least two groups were necessary for activity.

Among the ethylene oxides were found water-soluble compounds of high activity, but unfortunately biological effects were produced only with doses near to the maximum tolerated dose and this fact precluded their clinical use. It was among the ethylene imines, hundreds of which have been examined, that the most valuable effects were finally discovered simultaneously and independently by workers in Great Britain and the United States. The compounds were water-soluble, and had a high activity at a moderately low fraction of the maximum tolerated dose. They had a fairly high stability, so that it was found possible to give ethylene imines by mouth in the form of tablets. Chief among these compounds was *tris*-ethyleneimino-*s*-triazine, also known as 9500, and triethylene melamine (Figure 5).

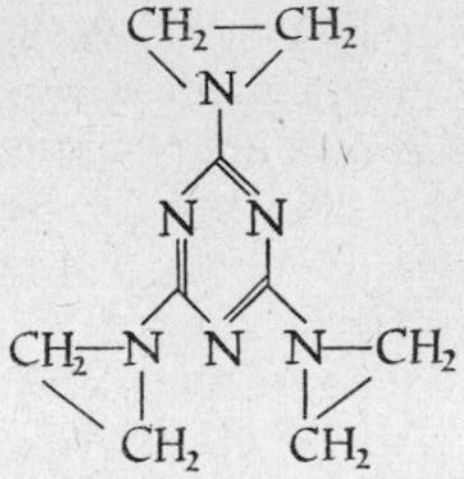

$$CH_2 - CH_2$$
$$\diagdown N \diagup$$
$$\mid$$
$$N \diagdown N$$
$$CH_2 - N \quad N \quad N - CH_2$$
$$\diagdown \quad \diagup$$
$$CH_2 \quad CH_2$$

Fig. 5. Triethylene melamine.

This drug has a palliative effect in leukaemia and Hodgkin's disease at least equal to that of any of the nitrogen mustards and has the advantage of causing less unpleasant toxic effects, and it is rapidly being accepted as one of the standard treatments for these diseases.

As a result of intensive work in this country a modified hypothesis for which there is experimental evidence has been ad-
vanced regarding the mode of action of all four types of radiomimetic compound so far mentioned. In order to understand
this a return must be made to textile chemistry, where it is found
that in addition to the simple cross-linking previously described,
the methylolamides, the ethylene oxides, and ethylene imines
also polymerize in the fabric to give coherent polymer chains in
the interstices of the fibre which impart a further rigidity to the
whole, as these interstitial polymers are linked by pendent reactive groups to the fibre chains. Furthermore, this property of
polymerization is at least as characteristic of these three chemical groups as is their reactivity as alkylating agents, to which
attention was just directed. The modified biological theory postulates that, for radiomimetic effects to be produced, a similar
state of affairs must take place in the cell and the drug must not
only be capable of cross-linking nucleoprotein chains; it must
also have the capacity of being absorbed into the cell as a relatively simple single molecule, and there polymerizing to give a
linear polymer having the necessary reactive groups spaced at
intervals along its length. In Figure 6 (overleaf) are shown the
polymers derived from:

(a) a nitrogen mustard $Cl—CH_2CH_2—N—CH_2CH_2—Cl$
                                                  $|$
                                                  R

(b) an ethylene imine $CH_2—N—R—N—CH_2$ (with CH_2 bridges)

(c) an ethylene oxide $CH_2—CH—R—CH—CH_2$ (with O bridges)

(d) a methylol amide $R(NHCH_2OH)_3$

Figure 6 (a) while a possible structure is hypothetical, no such
polymer having been isolated in the laboratory, but polymers of
types (b), (c), and (d) can be made in the laboratory and their
structures are established.

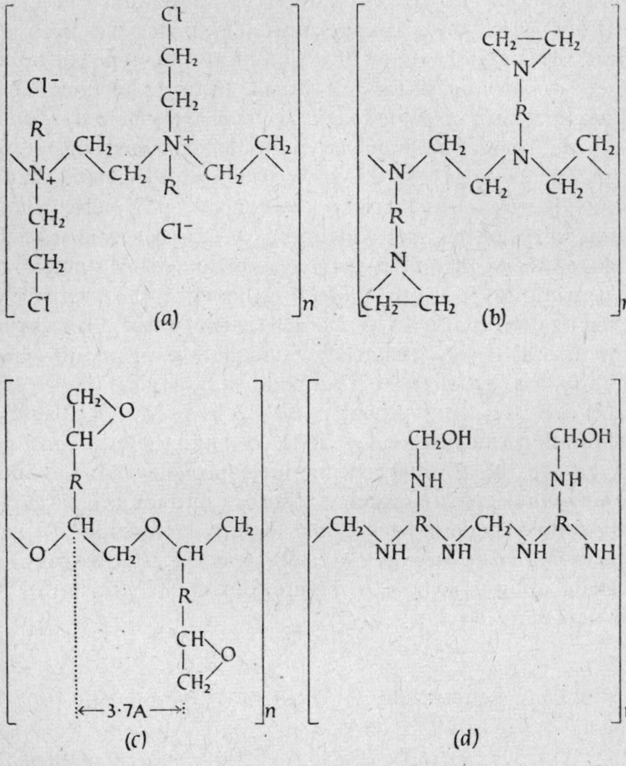

Fig. 6. Polymers derived from (*a*) nitrogen mustard, (*b*) an ethylene imine, (*c*) an ethylene oxide, and (*d*) a methylol amide.

The resemblance in general form between these polymeric structures is quite marked. The most important feature which they have in common is that the distance between two adjacent reactive groups along the 'backbone' is in all cases about 3.7A, though in the case of (*d*) a molecular model is required to see this clearly as it is caused by a three-dimensional spiral arrangement of reactive groups. There is considerable evidence in favour of this theory; thus it explains why many chemical compounds which are undoubtedly efficient cross-linking agents such as di-isocyanates are not radiomimetic agents since they cannot polymerize, and it explains why the nature of R has so little effect on activity as, as is evident from Figure 6, the size of R has no effect on the 'step distance' of 3.7A. But the chief evidence in its favour comes from a study of the methylolamides, where it is found that no compound having less than three —NHCH$_2$OH groups is active. Now while it is clear that a compound of the type HOCH$_2$NH—R—NHCH$_2$OH is a cross-linking agent and should on the earlier theory be active, reference to Figure 6 (d) will show that when a compound of this type is polymerized no free —NHCH$_2$OH groups remain. Hence the polymer produced is chemically inert and naturally inactive. Three or more methylol groups are required to give a polymer with free reactive groups along its length such as is given by di-functional compounds of the other three classes. Figure 7 is a simplified picture of a polypeptide chain, such as make up all proteins, and the similarity between this structure and the structures of Figure 6 is immediately apparent; again also a step distance of about 3.7A separates the pendent groups R which carry the acidic groups believed to react with the active moieties of the radiomimetic polymers.

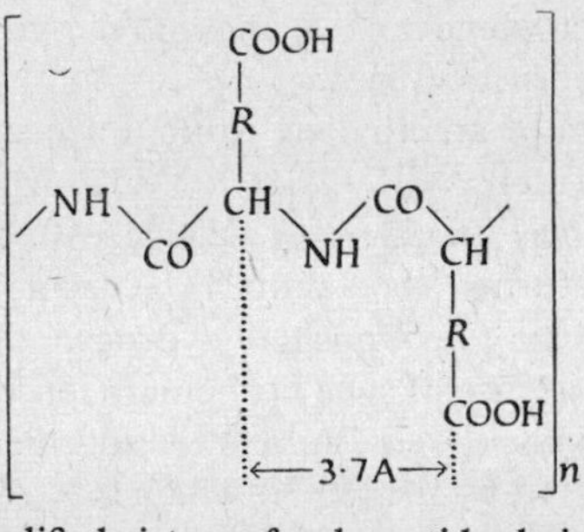

Fig. 7. Simplified picture of polypeptide chain (*cf*. Fig. 6).

A similar regular spacing of acidic groups, in this case phosphoric acid residues, occurs in the nucleic acids. The picture which results from this hypothesis is therefore of two adjacent nucleoprotein chains, in between which is a polymer chain, each pendent group of the polymer being bound to each pendent group of the nucleic acid or protein along its whole length, thereby giving a much stronger cross-link than would be given by the isolated single-molecule links of Figure 3.

Recently, however, a further class of radiomimetic agents of general structure $CH_3SO_2OCH_2$—R—$CH_2OSO_2CH_3$ has been discovered. These compounds are cross-linking alkylating agents capable of the same type of reaction as the other types of active compound. It is difficult to see how any polymerization of these compounds can occur and a second school of thought believes that all that is required for radiomimetic activity is that the drug shall give rise to a reactive positive ion, sometimes so unstable as to be formed only at the moment of reaction, similar to the immonium ion in the mustards. In the case of the last class of compound, the intermediate ion is of the type

$$^+CH_2RCH_2{}^+$$

formed transitorily by displacement of the methylsulphonyl (CH_3SO_2O—) groups by the groups in the nucleoprotein (e.g. —COO^-), with which the drug then combines to form the structure —$COOCH_2RCH_2OOC$—. Similar positive ions, called carbonium ions, are formed by the methylolamides, the ethylene oxides, and the ethylene imines, and all react rapidly with carboxylic or phosphoric acid ions.

The ionic form of an ethylene oxide, formed by opening the ring, may be written $^+CH_2$—$CH(R)$—O^-, which by reaction with —COO^- gives the ester —$COOCH_2$—$CH(R)$—O^- which simultaneously forms the neutral molecule —$COOCH_2$—$CH(R)OH$ by picking up a positive hydrogen ion, H^+, from the cell fluid. The existence of such carbonium ions as intermediates in organic reactions is well established, and their reactivity can be readily measured by the rate at which they react with powerful acidic (negative) ions such as the thiosulphate ion, to form an ester. It has been shown that there is some correlation between radiomimetic potency and the rapidity with which radiomimetic drugs react with thiosulphate ions in aqueous solution, thus leading to the conclusion that biological activity is directly related to the ease with which the drug can assume an ionic form. It is clear that there is evidence in favour of both theories, the active methanesulphonyloxy compounds falling outside the 'polymerization hypothesis', and the inactive di-functional methylolamides falling outside the 'carbonium ion' hypothesis. Neither theory explains all the facts, and both are probably very much over-simplified pictures of what actually occurs in the body.

In the introductory paragraph it has been remarked that whereas massive doses of radiation kill cells, weaker prolonged doses may give rise to malignant mutants. It is therefore of considerable interest that the chemical radiomimetic agents are also mutagenic and can be made to cause cancer. Repeated daily painting of the skins of rats with very small amounts of the compound shown in Figure 8 causes malignant tumours, and it has also been shown that prolonged injection of minute doses of nitrogen mustard will give rise to cancers in mice. A large proportion of the cells in tumours so induced show 'specific chromosome effects' during their division, and these abnormalities appear to persist during the whole life of the tumour, long after administration of the causative agent has ceased. In respect of their cancer-producing properties these compounds resemble the older carcinogenic hydrocarbons such as dibenzanthracene, though apparently in no way chemically related to them, and furthermore the carcinogenic hydrocarbons do exert an inhibiting effect, albeit somewhat smaller, on the growth of experimental animal tumours. The mode of action of the hydrocarbons is obscure and may or may not be related to the mode of action of the compounds under consideration.

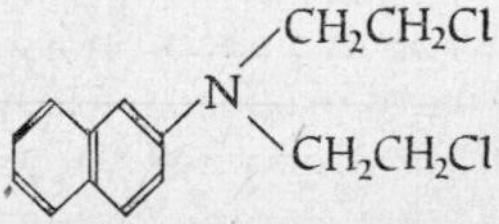

Fig. 8. This substance, N : N-*bis*-(β'-chloroethyl)-β-naphthylamine, has been shown to produce malignant tumours in rats.

While so far only compounds having more than one reactive group have been considered, considerable interest has recently been aroused in compounds carrying a single such group, which have been shown to be potent carcinogens. The long-chain ethylene imine shown in Figure 9 has been found to produce tumours in experimental animals receiving repeated small doses by injection. Recently also it has been shown that in doses of the order of 50 to 100 times that of related di-functional compounds these mono-functional compounds elicit weak specific chromosome effects, though, with one or two so far not satisfactorily explained exceptions, they have no tumour-inhibiting activity. It is of interest to record that ethylene oxide itself, one of the simplest of this class of compound, was shown independently in Russia to be a mutagenic agent causing mutations in the fruit fly.

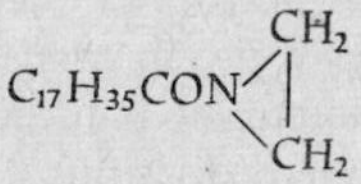

$$C_{17}H_{35}CON \overset{\textstyle CH_2}{\underset{\textstyle CH_2}{\diagup \atop \diagdown}}$$

Fig. 9. Long-chain (N-stearoyl) ethylene imine found also to produce tumours in experimental animals.

It is clear that the effects caused by these mono-functional compounds cannot be due to any form of cross-linkage, and an alternative explanation of their relatively very weak effects is that they do not link together the nucleoprotein chains, but 'plate' the surface of each chain separately with a layer of drug molecules, thereby inhibiting enzymic action on its surface.

It is evident from the work described that control of cancer and production of cancer are closely allied, and that the same chemical under different conditions of dosage may either cause a cancer or have an inhibiting effect on its growth according to the degree of cell-damage produced. The problem which confronts research workers is now to synthesize a radiomimetic compound which, because of some peculiarity in its structure, will be preferentially absorbed by the tumour, so concentrating its destructive effect where it is needed. This has not yet been achieved. The many hundreds of compounds so far investigated have an overall toxic effect on all the cells of the body, and, while their effect on the malignant cells is more marked than on normal cells, this is because of the much greater rate of division of the former. Although clinical evaluation of a number of these compounds has shown that a certain degree of control of malignant processes, especially of the blood and lymphatic systems, can be effected by chemotherapy, without undue interference with normal bodily function, little further progress is likely except by chance discoveries, until there is found some difference in the chemical structure or functioning of malignant cells compared with normal cells, which will enable chemists to produce drugs with structures capable of taking advantage of this difference and so concentrate in the malignant cell.

ACKNOWLEDGEMENT

The author is indebted to Mr C. H. Ockey, Dr A. L. Walpole, and Mr E. Young for the photographs reproduced as Inset 16 to 19.

FURTHER READING,

The following are two review articles which list most of the original work:
Philips, F. S. *Pharmacological Review*, **2**, 281 (1950).
Hendry, J. A. *Reports on Progress of Applied Chemistry*, **36**, 182 (1951).

INTERFEROMETRY IN ASTRONOMY

W. H. MARSHALL

INTERFEROMETRY is old and respectable as a branch of science. As an addition to the methods of classical astronomy, it is past its first youth, though still capable of new ideas. In the new branch of radio-astronomy, it has become an essential means of observation, and is at the stage of vigorous adolescence, passing rapidly into manhood.

The science of interferometry began in 1807, when Thomas Young performed his famous experiment, the principle of which is shown in Figure 1. Light from a source L passes through two

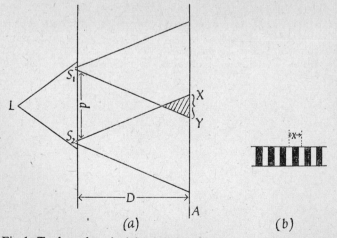

Fig. 1. To show the principle of Thomas Young's experiment: where the two beams in (a) overlap, in the region XY, bands of light and shade are produced, as shown in (b).

slits S_1 and S_2. Each of these slits becomes a secondary source, from which a beam spreads out, to fall ultimately on a screen A. In the region XY, where the beams overlap, we find bands of light and shade, as in Figure 1*b*. These bands are called interference fringes.

The ability of two (or more) beams of light to add together to make both light and shade arises from the nature of light. A ray of light is accompanied by a variable electromagnetic field, whose electric and magnetic components are perpendicular to each other and to the direction of the ray. These components vary simultaneously in a way which may be represented by a wave such as that shown in Figure 2. This wave may represent either the field strength at neighbouring points at the same instant, or the strength at one point at successive instants. In any case, the distance between successive crests (or troughs) is the wavelength λ, the height of a maximum above the mean level is the amplitude a, and the intensity of the light is proportional to a^2.

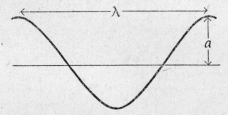

Fig. 2. The intensity of the wave is proportional to a^2.

Everyday experience shows that when two beams of light cross each other, neither is affected in any noticeable way. If this were not so, it would be impossible for two boys to watch a football match through one hole in a fence; indeed, it would be impossible for us to see anything clearly at all, because of the confusion produced by criss-crossing beams of light from all around us. Thus it is clear that when two light-waves are at the same point, the strength of the electromagnetic field at that point is the algebraic sum of the individual strengths. Figure 3 shows the situation at such a point, (*a*) when the two waves are in phase with each other, and (*b*) when they differ in phase by $\frac{1}{2}\lambda$. For simplicity, the waves are taken to be equal both in wavelength and in amplitude.

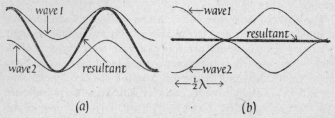

(*a*)   (*b*)

Fig. 3. The addition of light waves: (*a*) in phase, (*b*) differing in phase by $\frac{1}{2}\lambda$.

In the first case, the waves reinforce each other, and the resultant is a wave of the same wavelength and double the amplitude of either component. The intensity of the light is thus four times that of the uniform illumination from either beam alone. In the second case, each positive amplitude is opposed by an equal negative one, the resultant being zero amplitude, and so also zero intensity.

It will be clear that, if the phase difference between the two waves is not constant, the resultant will be continuously changing in intensity at every point. The fringes will oscillate across the screen at such a speed that the visible result will be uniform illumination. It should be noted that changes of phase do not matter, so long as both of the overlapping beams change by the same amount and at the same time. The two beams must, in other words, be coherent. Now, the light from any source changes phase frequently and abruptly, and two independent emitters could be in phase with each other only very rarely and for a very short time. In fact, the only way to obtain two coherent beams of light is to derive them both from one original source; and this is the reason for the arrangement shown in Figure 1*a*, and for the large number of different ways adopted by the designers of interferometers for splitting a single beam of light.

We have seen that two coherent beams of light, when they overlap, will produce light if they differ in phase by an integral number of wavelengths, and darkness if they differ by an odd number of half-wavelengths. In most interferometers, the phase-difference is produced by a difference in the length of path traversed by the beams. Thus, taking the dimensions shown in Figure 1, we can calculate the positions of the bright and dark fringes. The central fringe is bright, and equidistant from the slits, and the distance between successive bright fringes is $x = D\lambda/d$, where λ is the wavelength of the light. It should be noted that the separation of the fringes can be changed by changing that of the slits.

The chief astronomical applications of interferometry, at least until recent years, were achieved by A. A. Michelson's stellar interferometer. This instrument has been used both for the study of close double stars,* and for the direct measurement of the diameters of single stars.

For the first of these applications, the instrument is used in the modification due to J. A. Anderson. It then consists essentially of a plate, capable of rotation, and carrying a pair of slits whose separation can be varied. This plate is placed in the converging beam of light from the objective of a telescope, and so provides the required pair of coherent beams, which overlap and form an interference pattern in the focal plane. When the telescope is directed towards a close double star, each star produces its own system of fringes, their central bright bands occupying the positions where the images of the stars would be if the telescope were used without the interferometer.

Now, a telescope objective of focal length F, when directed towards two stars separated by an angular distance θ, will form in its focal plane two images with a linear separation $y = F\theta$. With the interferometer in position, therefore, the central fringes of the two systems are separated by this same distance $F\theta$; and we know that the distance between the centre of a bright fringe and that of a neighbouring dark fringe is $x = F\lambda/2d$, where λ is

*See article on 'Double Stars' in *Science News 24*.

in this case the 'effective wavelength' of the light from the double star. Thus, if we can make $x = y$, the bright bands of one system will fall on the dark bands of the other, and the interference pattern will disappear. When this happens, we have $F\theta = F\lambda/2d$, i.e. $\theta = \frac{1}{2}\lambda/d_0$, where d_0 is the critical separation of the slits. The separation d_0 can be measured, and λ can be determined from the colour or spectrum of the star, so we can calculate θ, the angular separation of the stars. Since the fringes are most distinct when the line joining the two stars is parallel to the line joining the slits, it is possible at the same time to determine the position angle, i.e. the angle between the north direction and the line joining the two stars.

The advantage of the interferometer for this kind of work is, that it doubles the resolving power of the telescope, and makes it possible to measure stars twice as close together in the sky as the limit possible with the telescope alone. And this advantage can be increased by observing not the total disappearance of the fringes but their decrease in visibility as the slits are moved apart. By extrapolating the visibility-curve, d_0 can be found even when it is far beyond the actual physical separation possible with any given instrument. The chief disadvantages are loss of light (which it shares with most other interferometers) and slowness and clumsiness in use.

The first disadvantage can be overcome only by attaching the instrument to a larger telescope. The second has recently been overcome by W. S. Finsen at Johannesburg, whose eyepiece interferometer is only a few inches long and is attached externally to the telescope as its name suggests. This instrument enables observations to be made much more quickly than before, and it may well give the stellar interferometer a new lease of life among observers of double stars.

However important the interferometric study of double stars may yet be, it remains true that the second application of the stellar interferometer has been the more important. The stars are so far away that, in spite of their great diameters, they are effectively point sources beyond (in most cases very far beyond) the resolving power of even the biggest telescope. We have seen, however, that in double-star work the interferometer can greatly increase the resolving power of any telescope; and the diameters calculated from the physical characteristics of some of the red giants suggested that they might well be measurable with a big instrument of this sort.

The principle of the method was suggested by Michelson in 1890, but it was not until 1920 that he and F. G. Pease designed and built the instrument with which the first measures were made. It consists of a 20-ft girder, carrying four 12-in. mirrors, and attached to the end of the tube of the 100-in. telescope at Mount Wilson, as shown in Figure 4. The two inner mirrors are fixed, the two outer ones are movable. Thus, the beam of star-light is split by the two outer mirrors into two beams, which in turn are reflected by the inner mirrors down the telescope tube. After reflexion from the primary and secondary mirrors of the telescope, the beams combine in the focal plane to form a disc crossed by interference fringes. The outer mirrors are set fairly close together, and moved apart until the fringes disappear, when the critical distance can be measured, and the angular separation of the two sources calculated.

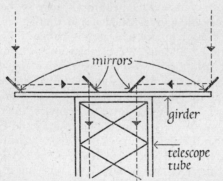

Fig. 4. Principle of the beam interferometer built for the 100-inch telescope at Mount Wilson.

But where are the two sources, when we are observing a single star? In this case we regard the disc of the star as consisting of two semi-circles. Then the light from each of these may be considered as coming from the centre of area of the half-disc, so that we have in effect two sources 0.41α apart, where α is the angular diameter of the star. When this value is substituted in the formula $\theta = \frac{1}{2}\lambda/d_0$ given above, we get $\alpha = 1.22\lambda/d_0$ for the angular diameter. This, however, assumes that the disc is uniformly illuminated, which is unlikely to be the case. The brightness of a stellar disc probably falls off towards the edge in much the same way as does that of the sun, as shown in Inset 10. When allowance is made for this 'darkening towards the limb', the angular diameter becomes $\alpha = 1.43\lambda/d_0$.

The diameters measured with this instrument range from $0''.020$ for Arcturus to $0''.047$ for Mira and Betelgeuse; and the corresponding linear diameters, taking their distances into account, range from 27 times that of the sun for Arcturus to 450 times for Antares. Another interesting result obtained is, that the diameter of Betelgeuse varies between 210 and 300 solar diameters, which may explain the well-known fact that the light of this star is subject to irregular fluctuations. The important point about the results, however, is that they all agree quite closely with the values calculated from theory, so that they confirm the theory and give us confidence in its other results.

In 1925, a 50-ft interferometer was designed by Hale and Pease. As erected at Mount Wilson, this took the form of a cantilever bridge with a somewhat limited range of movement. But even this bigger instrument was limited in its application, since it could reach no stars fainter than about fourth magnitude. It seems, in fact, unlikely that these large optical interferometers will add much more to our knowledge of the stars; but we must remember that they have done work of the highest importance, which could not have been done in any other way.

The next interferometer to interest us is also due to Michelson – the one used in the famous Michelson-Morley experiment on the reality or otherwise of aether drift. The experiment is not directly a part of astronomy; but it played a very important part in the development of the theory of relativity, and this theory has had so much influence on cosmology that it is almost as much a part of astronomy as of physics. Also, the three crucial tests of the theory are all astronomical in nature, and astronomers are still busy from time to time investigating these tests – and disagreeing about them.

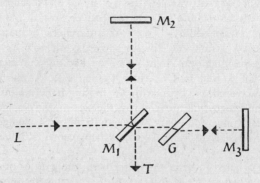

Fig. 5. Simple form of the Michelson interferometer.

In the simple form of the Michelson interferometer, as shown in Figure 5, the light from an extended source S falls first on a half-silvered mirror M_1. (A half-silvered mirror is one on which the silver coating is just thick enough to reflect half the light falling on it, the other half passing through it.) This splits the beam into two parts, one of which is reflected towards M_2, the other passing on to M_3. From these mirrors, the light is reflected back to M_1, which again divides each beam into two parts. The transmitted half of one and the reflected half of the other now travel together to T, where they form interference fringes, which may be either examined with a telescope or recorded on a photographic plate. The glass plate G serves to equalize the optical paths of the two beams to enable fringes to be observed with white light. It is clear that one beam passes through the mirror M_1 three times, the other only once. The first therefore suffers more dispersion than the other, and the result is to destroy the interference pattern. The slab G, cut from the same plate of glass as M_1, restores the balance.

Now, we have seen that in any interferometer, a bright band appears where the paths of the beams are equal or differ by an integral number of wavelengths, while a dark band appears where the path-difference, which we may now write as Δ, is an odd number of half-wavelengths. Let us take two such fringes, from which $\Delta = n\lambda$, and $(n - \frac{1}{2})\lambda$ respectively. If now the path of one beam is increased by $\frac{1}{2}\lambda$, the path-differences for these points become $(n + \frac{1}{2})\lambda$ and $n\lambda$. In other words, we now have dark where we had light, and light where we had dark; in effect, the pattern has moved half a fringe to one side. As the path is further increased, say by moving M_2 in the Michelson interferometer, the fringes will move across the screen, the displacement being one fringe for every wavelength of path change. This makes it possible to measure small displacements by counting fringes.

In the original form of the instrument, the path of one beam is changed by moving M_2 by means of a micrometer screw; and the instrument was used in this form for comparing the standard metre with the wavelength of a spectral line. In the application which interests us here, the change was not in the linear path, but in the optical path.

If light is transmitted by a medium, the aether, which is at rest in space while the earth moves through it, we should expect the velocity of light relative to the earth to depend on the direction in which the earth is moving. There would then be a difference in optical path according to the orientation of the instrument, and this would produce a difference in phase, just as if the two waves had covered paths of different lengths.

In the relativity experiment, the two beams produced by the dividing mirror were reflected back and forth several times to increase the path-length. The whole instrument was mounted on a sandstone block which floated in mercury to reduce the danger of distortion and vibration. This block rotated slowly so that the beams were constantly changing their orientations relative to the direction of the earth's motion. Thus, if the velocity of light were in any way affected by the motion of the earth through a luminiferous aether, the relative optical lengths of the two paths should have been constantly changing, and the fringes changing position. To detect any such change, the position of the central bright band was noted every sixteenth of a revolution. No significant displacement was found.

This experiment has been repeated many times since Michelson and Morley's first attempt; and with one exception the investigators have all confirmed the null result. It has therefore been concluded that the velocity of light is independent of any movement of its source, and that no uniform motion of any material body through space can be detected by observations on the body itself. Einstein took these two conclusions as the fundamental postulates of the theory of relativity, whose importance in modern physics and cosmology can scarcely be over-rated. In cosmology, in fact, relativity has occupied such a dominant place that H. Bondi, in his recent book *Cosmology,* found it necessary to protest against a tendency to regard theoretical cosmology as a branch of relativity.

So far, the interferometers described have been instruments using two beams coming from the same source. But one of the most important, and one which has important astronomical uses, depends on the interference of multiple beams. This is the Fabry-Perot interferometer (Figure 6). In the middle are two glass plates, lightly silvered on their facing surfaces, and set accurately parallel to each other. The source, at left, is an extended one. Light from a point P on the source falls on the interferometer at an angle θ and by repeated reflexions within the air-space between the plates it is transformed into a bundle of parallel rays. These are then focused by a lens, and since they come from the same source, they produce an interference pattern. If the distance between the plates is $d,$ and the wavelength of the light is λ, then the rays will reinforce one another where $2d \cos \theta = m\lambda$ $(m = 1, 2, 3, \ldots)$. This condition is satisfied by all points on a circle centred on the point where the axis of the lens meets the screen, and so the fringes take the form of bright circles on a dark ground. This interferometer is very well adapted to the accurate comparison of the wavelengths of lines in a spectrum.

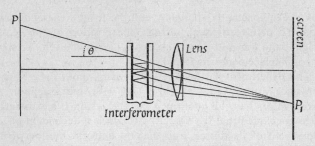

Fig. 6. The Fabry-Perot interferometer.

In the form described, the Fabry-Perot interferometer is best adapted for the production of fringes in monochromatic light. With white light containing many different wavelengths, each wavelength produces its own system of fringes, and so the result is confusion. To overcome this difficulty, the interferometer is used in conjunction with a spectroscope, so that the ring systems of the various lines in the spectrum are separated. Then, by the use of a slit over the source of light, a narrow band is isolated from each system, giving the sort of result shown diagrammatically in Figure 7a. Here, *A, B,* and *C* represent three lines in a spectrum, each line showing a set of Fabry-Perot fringes. It is possible to make very accurate comparisons of the wavelengths of the lines by measuring the radii of the rings.

The astronomical application of this method of measuring wavelength is complicated by the fact that the spectra concerned are absorption spectra, that is, they consist of a bright continuous background crossed by dark absorption lines. Now, if we think of the continuous background as composed of many narrow adjacent lines, we see that the appearance of the pattern will be something like Figure 7b. The lines are now so narrow that the rings are reduced to bright spots, and so close together that the spots form continuous bright channels on a dark background. Since the radii of the interference rings change from wavelength to wavelength, the channels are curved, their actual form being parabolic.

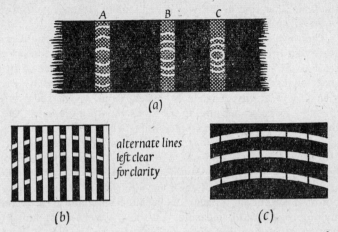

Fig. 7. To show the adaptation of the Fabry-Perot interferometer for astronomical use (see text).

Now suppose this bright spectrum to be crossed by dark lines, as in the cases of astronomical interest. Then the bright spots for the wavelengths of these lines will be missing, and the channels will be crossed by dark lines, as in Figure 7c. The measurement of these gaps in the parabolic channels yields very accurate values of the wavelengths of the absorption lines. For the most accurate results, the slit of the spectroscope is opened, so broadening the channels until they just coalesce, leaving a pattern of dark markings on a bright background.

A very important application of this method to the study of the sun's spectrum has recently been made by Miss M. G. Adam at Oxford. Fourteen lines in the solar spectrum were chosen, and their absolute wavelengths found by comparison with seventeen standard lines, ten due to oxygen in the atmosphere, and seven from a standard neon source. This determination was made for each line at thirteen points along the polar diameter of the sun's disc. A further refinement, suggested by P. J. Treanor, has made it possible to measure the solar lines and those of the sources at the same time, and in this way exceptionally accurate measures of wavelength have been made.

The wavelength of any line in the spectrum of the sun differs from that of the same line in a laboratory spectrum for three reasons. Firstly, it is shifted to the red by the influence of the sun's intense gravitational field – an effect predicted by the theory of relativity. Then it is shifted, either to the red or to the blue, by collisions among the atoms emitting the light. And finally, it is affected by Doppler shifts arising from the movement of the emitting atoms towards or away from the observer. Unfortunately, it is difficult to reconcile the observed wavelengths with values for all three of these effects, which will satisfy present theories of the solar atmosphere. The only way out of this difficulty appears to be the accumulation of more, and more accurate, measures of solar wavelengths; and at present Adam and Treanor's method of using the Fabry-Perot interferometer is the best means of obtaining them. The final result of this application of interferometry to astronomy will probably be a considerable refinement in our knowledge of the physics of the sun.

One of the difficulties which dogs all astronomers, except perhaps those who study the sun, is the lack of light. Much of modern astrophysics depends on spectroscopy, and in order to get spectra with a fair amount of detail in them the light from a star has to be spread out as far as possible without becoming too faint. The impossibility of using spectrographs of really high dispersion limits the study of the lines and bands in the stellar spectra, which might tell us much about the physics of the stars. Since the Fabry-Perot interferometer is such a powerful tool in this kind of work, it would seem that the use of this instrument would bring considerable advances here. But, unfortunately, the interferometer seldom passes more than about a thirtieth of the light which falls on it. Even the biggest telescope can scarcely collect enough light from even the brightest star to make such a loss of light tolerable.

It is only within the last few years that a way out of this difficulty has been suggested. S. Tolansky and J. Ranade have described a Fabry-Perot etalon giving fringes by reflexion instead of by transmission, which introduces very little loss of light, and so makes it possible to apply the instrument to the study of such faint sources as are found in astronomy. This is achieved by a very light silvering of the first plate, and a very heavy, opaque silvering of the second. The first coat then absorbs very little of the light passing through it, and the second gives a very bright reflected beam. The light lost is only a few per cent of the incident light, and so this instrument may well give valuable results in the spectroscopy of quite faint stars.

It is also worth remarking that interferometers are used nowadays in the testing of lenses and mirrors, so that astronomy may also owe to interferometry some of the improvement in its fundamental instruments.

Interferometry is contributing much, too, to the development of the youngest branch of astronomy, namely radio-astronomy. The traditional only link between the astronomer and his subject matter is light. Towards the end of the war, however, it became necessary to substitute for the word 'light' the wider term 'electromagnetic radiation', for it was found that the radiation from the sun and stars is not confined to that range of frequencies which affects the human eye. In addition to those radiations, which range in wavelength from a twenty-five-thousandth to about a twelve-thousandth of a centimetre, we can now detect radiations of wavelength from about eight millimetres to eighteen metres.* Now, these wavelengths are from ten thousand to ten million times those of visible light, and the difficulty of pin-pointing their source is also correspondingly increased. It was remarked by H. C. van de Hulst, in his recent Halley lecture, that 'The sharpness of ordinary eyesight could be equalled only by an instrument more than a mile in diameter' at radio wavelengths.

In these circumstances, the mapping of the sources of radio waves from the sky obviously demands the use of interferometry, and two types of interferometer have in fact been used in this

*See, for example, the article by A. J. Higgs in *Science News 21*.

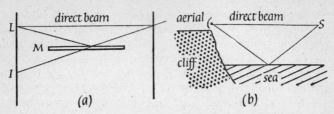

Fig. 8. To show the analogy between Lloyd's mirror (*a*), an early optical interferometer, and the type of radio interferometer (*b*) using sea reflexion. (In practice, the source, *S*, in (*b*) would be effectively at an infinite distance.)

work. The first is analogous to an early optical interferometer known as Lloyd's mirror. This was first described in 1834. As shown in Figure 8*a* this consists of a mirror, on which a beam of light falls at a very small angle, so that after reflexion it appears to come from *I,* the image of the slit *L*. The direct and reflected beams interfere, but instead of the full pattern of fringes like those in Figure 1*b,* the mirror gives only a half-system, with the 'central' bright band at one end. In the radio analogue, we have an aerial set on a cliff overlooking the sea (Figure 8*b*), so that once more, two coherent beams are produced, one direct and one reflected. As in the optical case, the interference pattern is a half-system, which may be represented by a sensitivity diagram (Figure 9), whose lobes correspond to the bright bands, while the spaces between the lobes represent the dark bands. The interference pattern thus takes the form of a set of favoured directions, the receiver giving a stronger signal when the source is in one of these directions than when it is between them.

Fig. 9. Polar diagram of sea-reflexion radio interferometer.

The Lloyd's mirror type of apparatus was introduced by J. G. Bolton and G. J. Stanley in Australia, and some very good work was done with it. It has, however, several disadvantages. It cannot be adjusted to cover the whole sky, observations being clearly restricted to a few degrees above the horizon. Its scope is thus rather limited, and at the small altitudes accessible to it, the radiation passes through the greatest possible thickness of atmosphere, and so the inaccuracies due to refraction are at their greatest. And finally, the dimensions of the instrument are limited by the availability of suitable cliffs. This limits also the resolving power, which is about four times that of a telescope of aperture equal to the height of the cliff.

These disadvantages are overcome in the spaced-aerial type of instrument, which corresponds to the beam interferometer in the optical case. The instrument consists of two aerials some distance apart, and capable of being rotated about an east-west axis to cover different regions of the sky. Thus, as the earth rotates, we may picture the sensitivity pattern of the aerial system sweeping across the sky at any desired height above the horizon. The outputs from the two aerials are fed into one amplifier, just as the optical rays from two slits are brought to the focal plane of the telescope. The sensitivity diagram in this

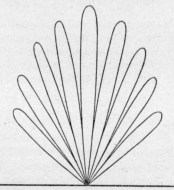

Fig. 10. Polar diagram of spaced-aerial radio interferometer; the weaker 'lobes' near the bottom of the diagram are not shown.

case looks like Figure 10, the central lobe corresponding to the central bright band with visible light.

After amplification, the output from the aerials operates a recorder, giving a trace which fluctuates in phase with the power of the received signal. So long as the source of the signal is large compared with the dimensions of the sensitivity pattern, the fluctuation is slow and of small amplitude. But a source which is smaller than the separation of the lobes of the pattern will give a distinct peak as it crosses each lobe. Figure 11 shows a part of the pattern which led to the important identifications described below. From the time of the central peak, the Right Ascension (corresponding to longitude on the earth) of the source or 'radio-star' is found; and its Declination (latitude) can be derived from the periodicity of the pattern.

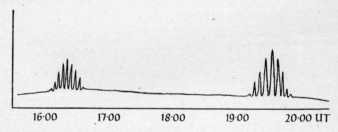

16·00	17·00	18·00	19·00	20·00 UT

Fig. 11. Section of record obtained at Cambridge with spaced-aerial, radio interferometer, showing the intense radio-stars in the constellation of Cygnus (16.20) and Cassiopeia (19.30). (*Copied from Ryle, Smith, and Elsmore,* Monthly Notices of the Royal Astronomical Society, **110,** 508 (1950), *by courtesy of the authors and of the society.*)

This work was done by M. Ryle, F. G. Smith, and B. Elsmore at Cambridge, with an instrument in which the aerials were spaced about 450 yards apart. This instrument is shown in Inset 11. Later, they used a special type of recording system, which evens out the background signal, and so makes it possible to record the patterns for radio-stars which would otherwise be too faint to be recorded. With this apparatus, they made a survey of the Northern Hemisphere of the sky, as a result of which a preliminary catalogue of fifty radio-stars has been published. The positions of these fifty stars are determined to within about half a minute of arc in Right Ascension, and five minutes of arc in Declination. These measures reduced the uncertainties in the position of the sources sufficiently to make it worth while looking for their visual counterparts; and the results have been extremely interesting.

The search was made both at Cambridge and at Palomar, and several objects were identified as occupying the positions of sources of radio waves. The radio-star in Cygnus was found to coincide with an extragalactic nebula of unusual appearance and peculiar spectrum. It has been suggested that this object is really a pair of galaxies in collision, and two further examples of the same type of cosmic catastrophe have been found. The intense source in Cassiopeia has been identified with a region filled with nebulous matter in streaming filaments moving at speeds of about thirty miles per second. This, and another object of the same kind, are located inside our own galaxy. Another of the radio-stars agrees in position with the Crab Nebula, which is an expanding shell of gas ejected by the explosion of a star in our own galaxy.

It is significant that where an identification has been possible, the sources of radio waves have been found to be associated with gases in violent, turbulent motion. The further understanding of the radio emission received from the sky will obviously be aided by further identifications of the objects which produce it. To add to these, the Cambridge workers have built a new and bigger interferometer, the following details of which have been kindly supplied by Mr Ryle. The aerial system consists of four similar units, arranged at the corners of a rectangle, to produce interference patterns in both Right Ascension and Declination. The east-west spacing is about six hundred yards, and the north-south spacing about fifty-five yards. Each unit consists of a cylindrical parabolic reflector, which focuses the radiation on to an 'aerial' along its axis. The total area collecting the radiation is about six thousand square yards.

We may well say that the advent of the radio-interferometer marks the coming-of-age of interferometry in astronomy. Previously, the interferometer was an interesting supplement to the really important instruments in the observatory – and in fact few working astronomers probably have ever seen one, and still fewer have used one. No matter how important the results are which have been obtained with them, the only interferometer which could ever hope to become an essential part of every observatory's equipment is Finsen's eyepiece instrument. No attempt has been made to improve on the fifty-foot beam interferometer at Mount Wilson, and even it is very little heard of. It may perhaps be felt that the number of stellar diameters already measured have given sufficient confirmation of the theory which enables them to be calculated. On the other hand, it is at least conceivable that further measures might reveal discrepancies leading to improvements of the theory. Yet we must admit that, so long as men, money, and materials are so urgently required for other work, the interferometer will just have to wait.

In radio astronomy, the position is quite different. Here, the interferometer is not a frill, or an occasional resort for some unusual problem – it is an everyday necessity, because it is the only instrument which can give sufficient resolving power to determine accurately the positions of the radio-stars. Thus interferometry may be expected to play a vital part in a new, exciting, and important branch of astronomy.

WEED CONTROL

IN all Britain's crops some 10 per cent by area is weeds, and they cost at least £50 million a year. The average loss of corn is guessed at 3 cwt the acre and it is thought that from 20 per cent to 25 per cent more could be got as a result of weed suppression by itself, regardless of other factors. In pasture there is the possibility of nearly doubling the production per season of desirable dry matter by optimum weed control. The competition of weeds with crops for light, air, water, and root-space is greater than is generally supposed, even with minor infestations. They have also technical disadvantages. Where there is rotation of crops, designed to check pests and diseases by sharp block-changes of habitat (as from cereals to brassicas), weeds persisting unchanged from crop to crop harbour them over and cancel the good effects. They greatly complicate mechanical harvesting of any type of crop by getting the mechanisms mixed up with fortuitous masses of vegetation which the designs cannot provide for. Finally weed-seeds spoil samples. Would you like wild radish in your porridge? Probably not, and millers reject many samples of oats because they contain wild radish seeds. On one acre a farmer will sow approximately 1¼ million seeds of wheat, oats, or barley, but that acre may contain up to 160 million weed seeds and it is usual for cereal seeds to be outnumbered by 100 to 1. The grass mixture the farmer sows will seldom have more than 12 million seeds to the acre, but individual species of the wild grasses he intends to replace can produce up to five times that amount. This potential weed population has to be prevented from becoming a real one, while the potential crop population has to be realized fully.

Crops ought to be grown in rotation, which rings the changes in type and time of cultivation from year to year and so controls a wide range of weeds. A fixed rotation has the merit of system-atizing weed-killing cultivations. But some aspects of the tech-nique are uncommercial. It cannot stand up to a depressed, capital-starved, or greedy agricultural situation, nor will it toler-ate violent fluctuations in the values of particular crops. Its trump card, the bare fallow employed when weeds really threaten to get on top, is often a failure in wet seasons, and involves the loss of a year's cropping. Much of the manual work which was an important part of the old rotations has been aban-doned because of high cost. It has gone completely in corn crops; and root crops, the so-called 'cleaning crops', which have to be hoed, are unpopular for the same reason. Weeds, therefore, could easily get life insurance were it not for the modern tech-nique of chemical weed-killing, in particular by selective herbi-cides.* They are outstandingly successful and cheap, and it is not surprising that, with the greatly increased tillage area we now have, the chemical industry has been able to build them up into a formidable sideline with astounding rapidity. The dis-covery of these substances has been empirical and there is often little knowledge of just how they kill weeds. Therefore only laborious testing of the many different ways of formulating and applying any weedkiller can show which is best – and it is neces-sary for instructions to be definite when complex techniques are sold to farmers. A lot of this work goes on, and somebody has to keep on top of it. Hence the 'Weed Control Joint Committee' – of the Ministry of Agriculture, the Agricultural Research Council, the National Farmers' Union, the Association of British Insecticide Manufacturers and the British Agricultural Contractors' Association. In November of last year this com-mittee got together the First National Weed Control Conference, the papers and discussions at which typified very interestingly the present stage in chemical weed control.

In wheat, barley, and oat crops the use of selective herbicides is now standardized and a wide range of weeds is controlled by the correct chemical applied at the correct stage of weed and

*Noted in *Science News 3,* 56.

crop growth. There are, however, still certain recalcitrant weeds. Wild Oats are very prevalent and there is no way of dealing with them. Their appearance and characteristics are indistinguishable from the cereals they infest, which means they cannot be cultivated out or selectively sprayed. Couch Grass, again, cannot be controlled in the crop and bare fallow is still the usual answer. There is, however, the possibility of applying sodium chlorate to the stubbles of couch-infested fields after harvest. This chemical will kill the couch and everything else, but the effect wears off in time to drill corn the following spring. Unfortunately it is expensive. Similar non-selective use can be made of trichloroacetic acid (T.C.A.). It is a grass killer and has been known as such since 1947. Commercial use is made of T.C.A. in the United States, but British use is still exploratory. It seems less lethal than sodium chlorate, but possibly cheaper. For the control of a wide range of weeds in beans, peas, and lucerne the newer spray 2:4-dinitro-6-secondary butyl-phenol (D.N.B.P.) is used. This is a more finely adjusted technique, which can in practice comprise balancing a possible crop damage against the removal of the weeds. For lucerne, chloro-isopropyl phenylcarbamate (C.P.C.) is now on the stocks, but is not yet at the practical stage. Corn is often undersown in the spring with the grass and clover mixture which is intended to occupy the ground after the cereal crop is harvested – thus making one seed-bed preparation do for two crops. In the past farmers have been enjoined not to spray such undersown cereals after the mixture has come through the ground, because of the supposed damaging effect of the herbicide on the clovers. Naturally many of them have ignored the recommendation and have found far less damage to the clovers than was expected. Speakers at the conference had accordingly looked again at the question and the conclusion is now suggested that spraying is practical. There will be damage, but it has been possible to indicate methods of spraying which will keep it low. The same technique can also be used in grass and clover mixtures sown alone.

About 70 per cent of the space contributing to human nutrition in Great Britain is grassland of one sort or another and weeds are estimated to cover 30 per cent of that space. These weeds, of course, reduce the nutritive product and sometimes poison the grazing animal. The physical fact of their spread wastes a lot of good herbage, because the animal will not take grass mixed with unpalatable weeds into its mouth. In this grass-land connotation 'weeds' can include certain species of grass, for there are productive and unproductive grasses. Probably more than 70 per cent of British grassland production comes from inferior plants. The problem is to eliminate them in favour of the productive grasses. This major alteration cannot be effected by the use of selective herbicides. Good management will establish a vigorous sward of the better grasses which will largely maintain itself against undesirable invasion. Selective killers, by knocking the non-grass weeds, assist this process of establishing and maintaining the better grasses. Previously all one could do with a weedy sward was to mow it, and that was not effective against prostrate weeds. There are various particular weeds of grassland to which attention is being paid. Rushes have always been mown or scythed and can be reduced provided the treatment is done annually. Heavy grazing of young rushes can have good effects if the cattle can be kept on them long enough to break up the clumps. Salt used sometimes to be broadcast on rushes to make them palatable for this purpose. Spraying with 2:4-di-chloro-phenoxy-acetic acid ('2:4-D'), one of the standard hormone weedkillers, combined with cutting a month before or after, gives a much better kill of common rush than these traditional processes.

Ragwort is widespread and poisonous, and accounts for many cattle and horses. It does not poison sheep, and grazing by sheep and taking a hay crop are the traditional methods of control. Experiments are in progress to determine the effect of spraying with '2:4-D' and 2-methyl-4-chloro-phenoxy-acetic acid (M.C.P.A.), the other standard hormone weedkiller. Existing plants can be killed. But ragwort land contains viable seeds which, to a depth of seven inches of soil, may amount to 5 million per acre. Their length of life in the soil seems to be about eight years. Unless, therefore, the sward is strong enough to

prevent their germinating, the elimination of ragwort by spraying will not be done in one season. Bracken may be controlled
by ploughing and cultivation, but it is a weed characteristic
mainly of unploughable land. It spreads almost entirely by
extension of rhizomes underground, which throw up the visible
fronds. Mechanical treatments – cutting, crushing, and so on –
can affect only the fronds. Continued for several years they
cause some death of rhizomes by weakening, but sufficient
always remain for regeneration. Thus there is scope for a
chemical herbicide if it will poison the rhizomes extensively.
Unfortunately neither selective herbicides nor total killers –
sodium chlorate and the newer 3-(p-chlorophenyl)-1, 1-dimethyl
urea (C.M.U.) – give better results than mechanical treatments,
except where the total killers are used at quite uneconomic rates.

Selective spraying of vegetable crops is carried out in the
United States, but only to a limited extent in Great Britain.
Vegetable crops hold the ground for short periods and involve
frequent and varying cultivations, which only a few weeds can
survive; in annuals, chickweed, annual nettle, fathen* and
annual meadowgrass; in perennials, couch, bindweed, and creep-
ing thistle. Onion seed-beds are sprayed with sulphuric acid
just before the onions emerge, and they can be sprayed again
when the onions have emerged and straightened up. This spray,
unfortunately, does not kill annual meadowgrass, which often
infests onion beds. Leeks can be treated similarly with good
results. Specially blended aromatic oils are used on carrots,
parnips, and parsley as selective sprays at various stages of crop-
growth. Weeding the carrot crop by hand on one's knees is a
dreadful labour and redoubtably expensive, so this technique is
a considerable advance. Parsnips grow slowly and therefore
require a clean habitat, which spraying may achieve more
cheaply than mechanical cultivation. Asparagus in the fern stage
may be sprayed with M.C.P.A., and potatoes before the haulm
is fully grown, but these procedures are not authenticated. Kale
as a farm crop is sprayed with sulphuric acid. At early stages the

*Pronounced 'fat hen'.

leaves are waxy enough to reject the acid which kills the surrounding weeds. Sugar-beet does not have a well-developed
cuticle in the early stages and cannot be treated with anything
that it does not tolerate physiologically. The beet crop is a bulk
crop; it ought to be harvested mechanically; it must therefore be
clean. Between the rows mechanical weeding is performed, but
in the rows hand-weeding is necessary. The crop also has to be
singled out to spaced individual plants, and the expense of that
can be cut either by very thin continuous seeding or by spaced
individual seeding. The highly refined brairds which result are
vulnerable to weeds and can easily disappear altogether. Chemical weed-killing in this crop would thus be the completion of an
over-all rationalization, but it again seems to be a question of
balancing the check to the crop (in final terms of sugar per acre)
against the effect on the weeds. Of the treatments reported on,
for instance, D.N.B.P. wiped out the crop, while others did not
kill enough weeds. However some of the experiments were described as encouraging.

A free growth of weeds and grass swards is accepted as part
of the cultural cycle for orchard fruits, and there is no evidence
of unrecognized loss to growers as a result of weeds. Possible
uses for herbicides would still be to reduce summer cultivations
and gang-mowing under the trees and to check undue growth
round the trunks. Selective herbicides could be valuable in soft
fruits, provided they did not affect quality. There is, however,
reluctance to initiate their use in fruit culture before fuller investigation of the ecological effects. The crop depends on natural
pollinating insects (as distinct from the hive bee), which might
suffer from any drastic alteration of the herbage.

In forest work, on the other hand, there have been interesting
and profitable applications of herbicides. Tree seedlings are
sown broadcast and grow slowly. When they are drilled in rows,
establishment per acre is less and mechanical cultivations between the rows are deleterious because of the soil disturbance
they cause. Hand weeding in nurseries comes to over £100 per
acre per annum and may cost up to £250. Up to one-fifth of the
seedlings are unavoidably removed by the manual work. Fallow

every third or fourth year is necessary and sooner or later weeds cause the abandonment of the nursery. These big costs are a powerful inducement to chemical methods, which need accordingly not be so cheese-paring as in ordinary farming. To destroy weed seeds in the soil before the tree seeds are broadcast, allyl alcohol, methyl bromide and ferric dimethylthiocarbamate are used. They succeed in strongly reducing weed growth without damage to subsequent crops of *some* tree seedlings and their effects on other species are under trial. The method is expensive and troublesome and the chemicals are unpleasant. Light mineral oils are used as contact sprays on weeds growing after the tree-seeds are broadcast but before they emerge. This is standard treatment in many Forestry Commission nurseries and reduces hand-weeding costs by between 40 and 70 per cent – a formidable saving at these ranges of expenditure. The oils can be applied to most hardwood and conifer seedbeds. After the tree seedlings emerge, mineral white spirits can be sprayed and greatly reduce weeding. Most hardwoods and some conifers are too sensitive for regular treatment with white spirits, and the extent of damage can sometimes be serious even in resistant species. The reasons are not yet understood, and therefore the technique is not generally adopted. Other sprays being tested on seedling-beds are: – ferrous sulphate, polychlor-aryl-alkyl-carbamate (P.A.C.), potassium cyanate; sodium 2, 4 dichlorophenoxyethyl sulphate (S.E.S.), and undecylenic acid. From the seedbed the tree goes to the transplant lines, and here it has developed resistance to white spirit sprays, which are therefore extensively used. They can be restricted to the soil surface and the stem bases of the transplants by hoods on the sprayer, which make any damage negligible. Finally the transplant is set out in the forest, and here there is little scope for chemical methods, since weeding costs are already low, varying from nil to £30 per acre. The main problem is ling heather, since ling-covered land is often naturally suitable for conifers and birch. If dumped straight into heather the young tree will not die, but it will not grow. The practice therefore is to plant on the upturned furrow slice of a deep ploughing and so give it a good start. Often the

heather is burnt off first. But it is always apt to re-establish itself
and the trees then get a check several years after being put out.
To avoid this, many chemical killers of ling have been tried. The
most successful are sodium chlorate, ammonium sulphamate,
sodium arsenite, M.C.P.A., and the isobutyl and ethyl esters of
'2:4-D'. These treatments have to be applied in large volumes
of oil or water and are impracticable on most of the terrains involved. Means of retaining the toxicity while reducing the
volume are being sought. Ultimately the forest is felled, and the
site may be let go for many years. The rehabilitation of such
derelict and scrub woodland can cost up to £50 per acre spent on
initial cleaning and dealing with the subsequent woody re-
growth. Ammonium sulphamate and sodium arsenite are being
tried on this scrub. Unfortunately, severe damage is of no value,
because regeneration occurs from the roots. Complete killers are
required and there is as yet no technique for getting at the roots.
Rhododendron ponticum (the common purple) is a particular
bugbear, since its waxy surfaces reject herbicides. Application of
sprays is difficult in these rough sites, and they are usually too
small for aerial cover. Nor can the question of amenity be
ignored when poisoning woodlands.

Finally, problems of application occupied the conference.
Spraying as a mechanical operation originated in the application
of various chemicals to crops expensive enough to pay for it. To
obtain adequate cover and penetration, large volumes of water
were used at high pressures. As the range of chemicals and crops
grew and the whole affair became cheaper, the question arose
whether these volumes were really necessary for distributing
a few pints of weedkiller. As a result, recommended volumes
now range from 1 to 120 gallons per acre. Moreover many types
of machinery are used and nozzles and pressures are multi-
farious. The net result is that the sizes of the droplets at which
sprays are applied vary widely. Does droplet size affect herbi-
cidal properties? In practice it does not seem to, and laboratory
results rather agree. However, the *selective* effect is very much
a matter of differing retention of the chemical by the leaves of
different plants, and in addition the spray may have to penetrate

foliage. Both retention and penetration are connected with droplet size. Spray nozzles, except for special types, do not give sprays of uniform droplet size. Any nozzle gives a range of sizes known as its 'droplet spectrum' and this always includes a number of fine droplets which will drift. A spray emitted 10 feet from the ground into a ten-mile-an-hour wind will drift coarse droplets 25 feet, fine droplets 150 feet, and 'fog' over a mile. It is this drift which kills neighbouring crops, gets round operators and poisons them, and stains the washing in villages. The booms of the sprayers can be covered in, which will cut out most of the drift if done properly, but makes it hard to see when nozzles get blocked. The nicer solution would be to impart an electrostatic charge to each droplet, but that is as yet a dream.

RESEARCH REPORT

A. W. HASLETT

COMPARATIVE BIOCHEMISTRY

RESEARCH on biochemical differences between species encounters one obvious difficulty in interpretation. The statement that 'whatever Miss T. eats turns into Miss T.' presents the main fact with almost startling simplicity. But it leaves it to be assumed either that cells of all forms of life are so completely alike that the conversion of one into another presents no problem; or alternatively that this facility on the part of Miss T. is wholly inherent, and that she would still remain chemically the same even though her feeding habits were those of tiger or seal. The extent of dietary influence can be determined only by observation, but it is at least to be expected that the molecular composition of any animal will be affected to some extent by that of raw materials absorbed as food, as well as by what it makes of its food when eaten.

Concentration on the second of these factors leads to the study of the enzyme systems of different organisms. The assumption is that enzyme systems are rather deeply embedded in hereditary make-up, so that any differences which are found will be a valid indication of evolutionary separation. Comparison of the protein-digesting enzymes of three species of amoebae, in fact, enabled N. Andresen and H. Holter of the Carlsberg Laboratory, Copenhagen, some years ago to resolve a problem in classification with at least as much plausibility as can be claimed from more usual lines of evidence. More obvious examples are afforded by various specialized groups of free-living bacteria which have become adapted to the use of other sources of energy than the oxidation of carbon compounds. But the general impression from the study of enzyme processes is rather of underlying similarity than of gross differences,* and such comparative work as has been done on higher animals has been mainly on chemical constituents, the over-all result of the food eaten, the modification of this by intestinal micro-organisms especially in mammals, and the enzyme systems of the animal. In the following notes, some recent examples are quoted, though without claim to completeness.

A new approach to the problem of chemical comparison has been described lately by J. J. Connell of the Torry Research Station, Aberdeen, of the Department of Scientific and Industrial Research. He has applied to the extractable proteins of fish muscle the method of separation known as electrophoresis, in which large molecules in solution are separated on the basis of their rates of migration in an electric field. The result is a succession of peaks of concentration which can be made visible and may partly overlap. In this way the patterns have been compared which are yielded by the muscle proteins of twenty species of fish representing several biological types, including bottom-living and free-swimming sea fish, and also four freshwater species. From six to twelve components have been found in different preparations, and 'the most striking fact emerging from this work is that considerable differences . . . occur from species to species, and that these differences are so characteristic as to fingerprint any one species'. On the other hand, merely from the appearance of the patterns it does not appear that there is necessarily any close relation between the patterns of closely related fish – for example cod, haddock, whiting, and coalfish (genus, *Gadus*), compared with plaice, lemon sole, and witch (genus, *Pleuronectes*) – although two species of skate show some resemblance.

Compared with this detailed but so far meaningless specificity, there is a broad appeal in the study of the means by which the

---

*Compare, for example, the general lack of success in the search for substances designed to have a blocking effect on metabolic processes essential to bacterial cells but inessential to the cells of the human body.

energy-yielding substance adenosine triphosphate is reformed after use in muscles. This was discussed by Professor E. Baldwin of University College, London, in his contribution to a symposium on evolution held by the Society for Experimental Biology and lately published. In general, the part in resynthesis which in vertebrates is played by creatine phosphate is played in invertebrates by arginine phosphate. But various complications have been found, some interesting, and others disturbing; and Professor J. B. S. Haldane, summing up, suggested that the distinction may yet prove 'as inadequate a label' in classification as has haemoglobin.

Possible connexions between chemical composition on the one hand and both systematic classification and, more doubtfully, with feeding habits on the other are suggested by a long series of investigations on fatty acids by Professor T. P. Hilditch and his colleagues at Liverpool University. The seed fats of plants have been studied in enough species to support the idea of a connexion between chemical classification and botanical, and the same is true to a lesser extent of fishes and sea-living animals. Less work has been done on land-living animals. A primary classification in terms of 'high' and 'low' proportions of stearic acid turns out to be not very satisfying; the 'high stearic' group including not only the flesh-eating felines and the ruminants, but also certain non-ruminants such as the camel and kangaroo. The most suggestive indication in the present context is perhaps the finding that various unsaturated fatty acids contained in badger fat 'are those found on the one hand in vegetable-fruit fats, and on the other in the fats of frogs and small amphibia, both of these sources being among the reputed common foods of the badger'. Although there is no general evidence for the effects from feeding habits which might be expected, they are at least a possible factor.

An interesting but more specialized example of a chemical difference between species has been brought to light lately through the work of Professor V. du Vigneaud and his colleagues in the Department of Biochemistry, Cornell University Medical College, on the hormones produced by the posterior

lobe of the pituitary gland.* Two of these hormones have lately
been synthesized: oxytocin, which makes the uterus contract
in childbirth and stimulates the ejection of milk, and vasopressin, which constricts blood vessels and increases the re-
absorption of water by the tubules of the kidney. Both of these
hormones are built up from amino-acids − being in fact polypeptides − and both contain a total of 8 amino-acids, 6 in the
form of a closed ring and 2 in a branched chain. They are built
on the same plan, and the difference between them is that one
each of the ring and side-chain amino-acids are different in the
two cases. The position in the closed ring which in oxytocin is
occupied by isoleucine is filled in vasopressin by either lysine
or arginine. It is here that the difference between species has
been found. Vasopressin obtained from pigs (hog vasopressin)
contains lysine, and that from bullocks (beef vasopressin) contains arginine.

The research at Cornell is still in progress. The position as so
far reported is that the structures assigned to these three substances are based on the same arguments: the break-down products and reactions obtained from purified natural products, and
the usual over-all analysis. In the case of two of them, oxytocin
and hog vasopressin, these structures have been confirmed in
the sense that syntheses based on them have yielded substances
which apparently are homogeneous and which show the same
biological effects as the natural hormones. (There has, in fact,
been uncertainty whether the same hormone, vasopressin,
affected both blood vessels and kidneys; du Vigneaud's work
confirms incidentally that this is the case.) The remaining link
to complete the argument will be to synthesize beef vasopressin,
with arginine in place of lysine, and to confirm that this, too,
shows activity as a hormone. But with two of the three structures
confirmed already by synthesis, and the evidence for the third
structure of the same kind, the case appears near enough to
being established. It is the more interesting that the comparative
biochemistry of polypeptides is still a little-explored subject,

*See article by Bernard Donovan in *Science News 30*.

although it may well prove relevant to the search for more specific antibiotics than those already available.

Connell, J. J. *Biochemical Journal,* **55,** 378 (1953).

Baldwin, E. 'Biochemistry and Evolution'. *Symposium of the Society for Experimental Biology: No. VII, Evolution.* Cambridge University Press, 1953.

Gupta, S., Hilditch, T. P., and Meara, M. L. *Journal of the Chemical Society,* 3145 (1950).

du Vigneaud, V., and others. *Journal of the American Chemical Society,* **75,** 4879 and 4880 (1953).

RATE OF PLANT EVOLUTION

The frequency with which plant species show chromosome multiplication, otherwise polyploidy, compared with the basic chromosome-number of their genus – that found in reproductive cells of the simplest species – is generally taken to be an indication of past activity in evolutionary development. A comparison on these lines has been made lately by Professor Irene Manton of the University of Leeds, between the fern flora of Ceylon, as representing a tropical climate, and those of Europe and Madeira. The preliminary results are summarized in the symposium on evolution mentioned in the previous paragraph. They are of interest in relation to earlier work showing that in western Europe the frequency of polyploidy increases from temperate latitudes northwards. This has been taken to suggest a connexion between polyploidy and cold, and especially with the last Ice Age. In the ferns of Ceylon, on the other hand, Professor Manton and her colleagues found that the percentage of polyploidy is higher than in Britain (60 per cent in some 130 species, compared with 53 per cent). The degree or grade of polyploidy is also higher, and this is illustrated in a detailed comparison of species of three genera. Professor Manton's interpretation is that 'evolution is proceeding (and has in general always proceeded) faster in the tropics than in temperate latitudes', and that 'the stimulus to species formation commonly associated with the Ice Age in Europe was a local and temporary one and was possibly more influenced by the recession of glacial conditions (giving unusual opportunities for recolonization of new habitats by new forms) than by the introduction of glacial conditions as such'. While the data presented are at least suggestive, it should perhaps be repeated that they relate only to ferns, and that comparisons between more countries and ranges of climate are clearly desirable – as indeed Professor Manton has herself recognized.

Manton, I. 'The Fern Flora of Ceylon'. *Symposia of the Society for Experimental Biology: No. VII, Evolution*. Cambridge University Press, 1953.

PILTDOWN MAN

The disappearance of 'Piltdown man' as a problem in human evolution will be already familiar to most readers of *Science News*. It should be said, therefore, that from the first description of these remains by Sir Arthur Smith Woodward in 1913 there has been uncertainty about their dating, and that the apparent association of an ape-like jaw with an essentially human cranium was the main reason which caused Sir Arthur Keith to propose that the material as a whole should be assigned to the earlier of two periods from which fossil remains of animals had been found in the Piltdown gravel. This period is now classed as Upper Pleistocene – surprisingly early for the cranium, but necessary in the view of Sir Arthur Keith to account for the ape-like jaw. The association was a real one in respect of finding; Sir Arthur Smith Woodward himself dug out a small portion of the skull from 'within a yard of the point where the jaw was discovered, and at precisely the same level'.

The difficulty of associating jaw and cranium was made greater by the discovery from 1927 onwards of successive fossils of Peking man (*Pithecanthropus*), a user of fire and maker of tools, but primitive in skull shape and yet roughly contemporary with the earlier of the dates suggested for Piltdown man; and, if their approach to humanity was accepted, by the near-men of

South Africa, most conveniently lumped together as australo-pithecines. It was made greater again when, in 1950, K. P. Oakley, of the British Museum (Natural History), and C. R. Hoskins, of the Department of the Government Chemist, reported the results of applying to the Piltdown fossils the fluorine method for the comparative dating of bones and teeth. The basis of this method is the progressive conversion of the chief constituent of bone, hydroxyapatite, into fluorapatite at a rate dependent on the concentration of fluorine in the soil water. It is because of this dependence that the method is comparative, and not absolute. With the quantities of material which it was then thought proper to use, these measurements, in comparison with those on other fossils from the same beds and district, disposed decisively of the earlier of the two dates suggested for 'Piltdown man'. They did not distinguish between the cranium on the one hand and the mandible (with two molars) and an isolated canine tooth on the other, or give any more precise indication than that the remains as a whole could not be earlier than Middle Pleistocene. The centre of interest at this time was the status of the South African australopithecines, and the revised dating of the Piltdown remains attracted less attention than it once would have.

The next and probably final stage resulted from a suggestion made in personal discussion by Dr J. S. Weiner of the Department of Anatomy, University of Oxford, that the mandible and an isolated canine tooth had been deliberately faked. He supported his suggestion by showing experimentally that 'artificial abrasion of the teeth of a chimpanzee combined with appropriate staining produced an appearance astonishingly similar to the Piltdown molars and canine'. At the time of writing the obvious personal question, 'Who did it?', has not been answered. But since 'Piltdown man' was already an embarrassment in the study of human evolution, the chief scientific interest lies in the physical and chemical methods which have been used to confirm this suspicion.

Full analytical details have yet to be published. But in its present improved form the fluorine method is shown to be capable of detecting a minimum of 0.01 per cent in a necessarily small sample taken from an isolated tooth. On the question of age, the fluorine method was reinforced by measurements of nitrogen, shown by S. F. Cook and R. F. Heizer in the United States to be lost by bones preserved under broadly the same conditions at a relatively slow and, on an average, almost uniformly declining rate. The nitrogen content of samples from the Piltdown material and selected controls was estimated by a method devised by J. D. H. Wiseman and Mrs A. Foster in the Department of Minerals of the British Museum. The lowest percentage reported from these tests was 0.3 per cent for an Upper Pleistocene human molar, and the results for the Piltdown mandible and teeth (from 3.9 to 5.1 per cent) confirm that they are modern.

Chemical and physical tests were carried out also to elucidate the iron and chromate staining of the Piltdown jaw. This is now thought 'to be explicable only as a necessary part of the deliberate matching of the jaw of a modern ape with the mineralized cranial fragments'. The examination for chromate is of further interest. As well as the direct method of chemical analysis, carried out in the museum by M. H. Hey and A. A. Moss, use was made of the non-destructive, x-ray spectrographic method devised by E. T. Hall of the Clarendon Laboratory, Oxford, and mentioned in *Science News 29* (p. 115). Other pieces of evidence came from a careful study of the teeth themselves, supported by deeper boring than would probably have been undertaken had not suspicion been already aroused. But the chemical and physical methods used carry an altogether higher order of conviction than could be obtained by subjective examination, however thorough. Still another method has, in fact, been tried, and the results obtained with it are now in course of publication.

Weiner, J. S., Oakley, K. P., and Le Gros Clark, W. E. 'The Solution of the Piltdown Problem'. *Bulletin of The British Museum (Natural History)*, Vol 2, No. 3 (1953).

CORRESPONDENCE

OCEAN-BED PROSPECTING

IN the article under the above heading in *Science News 29,* the authors state (p. 8) that only survey and research ships are fitted with deep-sea echo sounders. I feel that they overlooked the cable ships, which of course are vitally concerned with the topography of the sea-bed both in laying and repairing cables. I should like to suggest that the topographical side, at least, of ocean-bed prospecting would gain from a close co-operation between pure and applied science at an insignificant extra cost.

P. R. BRAY

Kenton, Middlesex

SUPERSONIC FLIGHT

DR LANCE in his recent article on supersonic flight appears to draw a clear distinction between air disturbances of a purely aerodynamic origin and those from other acoustic sources. He states that 'unless the aircraft was capable of sustained flight at about Mach 1.0, the sound of its engines, etc., would not accumulate'.

Though it may well be true that, at supersonic speeds and above, the major source of noise is aerodynamic, it must be remembered that all disturbances are propagated in an identical fashion, be they of aerodynamic origin or otherwise. Indeed, were it possible to exclude aerodynamic noise altogether, I fail to see any objection to expecting a bang from a pure source of noise travelling at supersonic speed by exactly that explanation which Dr Lance appears to limit to aerodynamic sources alone.

Later in his article, the writer describes how a double bang may be expected from a typical flight curve at supersonic velocity; he here states that '. . . the bang heard first will have been caused by the aircraft whilst at A_2, and that heard second will have been caused whilst at A_1'; A_2 being subsequent to A_1 on the flight curve. If the times taken for the bang to reach the observer from A_1 and A_2 are respectively t_1 and t_2, it would appear that, should the pilot be sufficiently energetic to deviate, still at supersonic speed, so as to arrive at A_2 after a time greater than $(t_1 - t_2)$ has elapsed since he was at A_1, then the converse of the above statement will hold; if the elapsed time is less than $(t_1 - t_2)$, the statement will of course be true, and if equal to $(t_1 - t_2)$, the bangs will arrive simultaneously. It is assumed that the velocities of the aircraft at A_1 and A_2 are unaltered in each case, so that the observer's position remains fixed.

H. A. HOPKINS

Cheltenham

Dr Lance writes:

The difference between 'aerodynamic' and 'acoustic' disturbances can be quite easily explained. A shell projected with a supersonic muzzle velocity causes bangs, during that part of its trajectory which is supersonic, in the manner described in my article. The shell causes aerodynamic but no acoustic disturbances since it has no engine to generate sound. The engines of an aeroplane, however, do generate sound, and if the aircraft is flying supersonically the sound will certainly accumulate, as Mr Hopkins rightly suggests. The point, which may not have been made sufficiently clear before, is that the acoustic noises do not accumulate sufficiently to cause bangs unless the aeroplane is travelling transsonically. This has been shown in one of the references given previously. Since the article was written my attention has been drawn to an almost complete account of 'Supersonic Bangs' written as long ago as 1925 : *L'Acoustique des canons et des projectiles* by E. Esclangon. The whole book of some 380 pages is devoted to a subject which I attempted to condense into 12 pages; for this reason a great deal had to be left unsaid, and I can only belatedly apologize for any important omissions.

With reference to the last point raised by Mr Hopkins. It is perfectly true that my statement with regard to Figure 3 is only true if the plane reaches A_2 before the bang generated at A_1 gets there. As the diagram was drawn there should have been no doubt about it, but had the plane looped the loop between A_1 and A_2 the statement would have required qualification.

SOME BOOKS RECEIVED

THE LANGUAGE OF SCIENCE by T. H. Savory (London: Andre Deutsch, Ltd, 1953), pp. 184, 10s 6d.

Mr Savory's book is described as the first 'broad study' of the language of science: its words, prose, origins and growth, and 'literature'. It is directed at philologists as well as scientists. The author's qualifications include a specialized knowledge of one branch of biology (broadened by teaching), acquaintance with Latin and Greek, and ability to write. For scientific readers the most useful chapters are on the history of their language. Here there is little room for argument, unless by a more extended study of origins. There is a subsidiary interest in Mr Savory's defence, primarily for philologists, of the use made of their language by scientists. The case for using specialized terms to convey specialized meanings is validly presented. But it would give a different impression if accompanied by some discussion of the need for review articles, written for not quite the most narrowly defined specialist, and by the advice of the Royal Society that an author should write 'not for the half-dozen people in the world specially interested in his line of work, but for the hundred or so who may be interested in some aspect of it if the paper is well written'.

CHEMISTRY AND MAN by Sir Cyril Hinshelwood, R. P. Linstead, the late Sir Jack Drummond, and J. W. Cook (London: E. & F. N. Spon, Ltd, and the Chemical Council), pp. 88, 7s 6d.

These four lectures on chemistry and modern thought, the amenities of life, food, and the conquest of disease make an interesting symposium; but although the book is said to be 'based' on the lectures, adaptation to printed form appears to have been slight, and some large gaps (e.g. metals) are not at all indicated by the title.

THE ART OF SCIENTIFIC INVESTIGATION by W. I. B. Beveridge (London: William Heinemann, Ltd, 2nd edn 1953), pp. 176, 10s 6d.

In the three years since its first publication, Professor Beveridge's book has become already established as one of the classics of science.

There is no other which discusses research, as such, from the point of view of those doing it, and there can hardly be another so well illustrated with first-hand and relevant anecdotes. Although written primarily for the young working scientist, it conveys incidentally to the outsider a more accurate impression of science as practised than could many volumes devoted to summaries of results. It should be a 'must' for administrators whose decisions may affect research.

GAS TURBINES AND THEIR PROBLEMS by Hayne Constant (London: Todd Publishing Group, Ltd, 1953), pp. 160, 17s 6d.

As Director of the National Gas Turbine Establishment, Mr Hayne Constant is well placed to write an authoritative review of the gas turbine, which he points out should be regarded, not as any one kind of engine, but as a system comprising at least a compressor, heater, and turbine, and possibly several of each, as well as heat exchangers. He writes simply and directly, primarily for engineers; and, although a multiplicity of actual and possible designs makes the material to be discussed complicated, demands on special knowledge are slight. Personal judgements and opinions are freely expressed, but the general impression is of a 'down to earth' book. 'For some years to come the crying need will be for operating experience on components.'

NEW CONCEPTS IN FLOWERING-PLANT TAXONOMY by J. Heslop-Harrison (London: William Heinemann, Ltd, 1953), pp. 135, 6s.

Although the classification of plants, for the purposes of practical identification and the exchange of observations, and the study of their evolutionary relationships and present plasticity as a contribution to biology, should ideally go hand in hand, there is likely to be a difference in emphasis and approach, at least for a long time to come. Dr Heslop-Harrison's introduction to experimental methods and their interpretation should do much to encourage interest; this should be a useful book, provided that the gap between present and future is borne clearly in mind.

FRESHWATER MICROSCOPY by W. J. Garnett (London: Constable and Co., Ltd, 1953), pp. 300, 30s.

Mr Garnett's introduction to the microscopy of freshwater ponds would be notable alone for its 50 well-produced plates. It has the further merits that it is based on personal observation, and includes all forms of life from algae and protozoa to higher plants and insects. It is so written as to be of value both to university students and amateurs.

VIRUSES IN MEDICINE (*British Medical Bulletin,* Vol. 9, No. 3: London, British Council, 1953), pp. 56, 15s.

Edited by Dr Forrest Fulton, of the London School of Hygiene and Tropical Medicine, and with contributions by Dr C. H. Andrewes, Sir Macfarlane Burnet, and Professor A. J. Rhodes of Toronto among others, this is a particularly well-planned symposium. Five articles on some of the more general aspects of human viruses should be intelligible to most readers of *Science News,* and include a summary, by Dr Fulton, of techniques of research. These are followed by accounts (which on the whole are more technical) of work on ten or so particular diseases, including smallpox, poliomyelitis, epidemic influenza, and the common cold, with a final contribution on veterinary diseases of medical interest.

ABOUT OUR CONTRIBUTORS

R. N. HIGINBOTHAM was educated at Harrow and Trinity College, Cambridge. Aged 32, he has farmed in Sussex since 1946, and has been a previous contributor to *Science News* on farming topics.

P. E. HODGSON graduated in physics at the Imperial College of Science and Technology, University of London, in 1948; worked on cosmic radiation (Ph.D., 1951) under the direction of Professor Sir George Thomson; and is now engaged in research in nuclear physics at University College.

R. F. HOMER was born in 1926, and educated at Dudley Grammar School and Birmingham University, where he did research on the possible chemotherapeutic uses of sugar derivatives under the Colonial Research Council, obtaining his Ph.D. in 1945. He then joined Imperial Chemical Industries, Ltd, and has since worked on problems in chemotherapy, particularly in the cancer field.

W. H. MARSHALL, graduate of Glasgow University, Fellow of the Royal Astronomical Society, Vice-President of the Scottish Branch of the British Astronomical Association, worked on explosives during the war and is now principal teacher of science at a school near Kilmarnock.

J. F. PEARSON, aged 31, was educated at the Universities of Liverpool and Cambridge. He spent some years in research and development at Imperial Chemical Industries, Ltd, General Chemical Division, Widnes, and at Lever Bros, Ltd, Port Sunlight. From 1951 until 1953 he was a lecturer in chemical engineering, Loughborough College of Technology, and is now a lecturer in engineering in the University of Manchester concerned with research in heat transfer and automatic control.

A. M. TURING, O.B.E., F.R.S., is Reader in the Theory of Computing at Manchester University. Before the war he was engaged in research in mathematical logic.

INDEX

FOR NUMBERS
28–31

SUBJECT INDEX
Numbers 28–31

References are in all cases to page and number, e.g., 29(24). Articles are indexed under what is judged to be a key-word in their titles (printed in small capitals). Cross-references are suggested under a number of general subject names. Paragraphs under the heading *Research Report* are indicated by (*R.R.*). Continuing references are, in general, not given.

INDEX OF AUTHORS
Numbers 28-31

Further information about any author is to be found in the column *About our Contributors*, which appears in each issue. The numbers in brackets indicate the number of the volume.